REVISE FOR

D0532800

Edexcel

GCSE MATHEMATICS

FOUNDATION

Keith Pledger   David Kent

About this book

This book is designed to help you get your best possible grade in your Edexcel GCSE Mathematics examination. The authors are the Chair of Examiners and the Development Manager for Mathematics, and have a good understanding of Edexcel's requirements.

Revise for Edexcel GCSE: Foundation covers key topics that are often tested in the Foundation level exam papers, focusing mainly on grades D, E and F. *Revise for Edexcel GCSE Mathematics: Intermediate* Focuses mainly on grades B, C and D, whilst *Revise for Edexcel GCSE Mathematics: Higher* is focused on Grades A*, A and B.

You can use the book to help you revise at the end of your course, or you can use it throughout your course alongside the course textbook: *Edexcel GCSE Mathematics: Foundation* which provides complete coverage of the syllabus.

Helping you prepare for your exam

To help you prepare, each topic offers you:

Key points to remember – These summarize the mathematical ideas you need to know and be able to use.

Worked examples and examination questions – help you understand and remember important methods, and show you how to set out your answers clearly.

Revision exercises – help you practice using important methods to solve problems. Past paper questions are included so you can be sure you are reaching the right standard, and answers are given at the back of the book so you can assess your progress.

Test yourself questions – help you see where you need extra revision and practice. If you do need extra help they show you where to look in the *Edexcel GCSE Mathematics: Foundation* textbook.

Exam practice and advice on revising

Examination style practice paper – this paper at the end of the book provides a set of questions of examination standard. It gives you an opportunity to practice taking a complete exam before you meet the real thing.

How to revise – For advice on revising before the exam, read the **How to revise** section on the next two pages.

How to revise using this book

Making the best use of your revision time

The topics in this book have been arranged in a logical sequence so you can work your way through them from beginning to end. But **how** you work on them depends on how much time there is between now and your examination.

If you have plenty of time before the exam (at least 8 weeks) then you can **work through each topic in turn**, covering the key points and worked examples before doing the revision exercises and Test yourself questions.

If you are short of time then you can **work through the Test yourself sections first** to help you see which topics you need to do further work on.

However much time you have to revise in, make sure you break your revision into short blocks of about 40 minutes, separated by five or ten minute breaks. Nobody can study effectively for hours without a break.

Using the Test yourself sections

Each Test yourself section provides a set of key questions. Try each question:

If you can do it and get the correct answer, then move on to the next topic. Come back to this topic later to consolidate your knowledge and understanding by working through the key points, worked examples and revision exercises.

If you cannot do the question, or get an incorrect answer or part answer, then work through the key points, worked examples and revision exercises before trying the Test yourself questions again. If you need more help, the cross-references beside each test yourself question show you where to find relevant information in the *Edexcel GCSE Mathematics: Foundation* textbook.

Reviewing the key points

Most of the key points are straightforward ideas that you can learn: try to understand each one. Imagine explaining each idea to a friend in your own words, and say it out loud as you do so. This is a better way of making the ideas stick than just reading them silently from the page.

As you work through the book, to go back over key points from earlier topics at least once a week. This will help you to remember them in the exam.

Working on the worked examples

Read each question at the start of each worked example and think about what it is asking you to do. Try to work out which key point(s) you need to use, and how to answer the question before you look at the answer itself.

The answer will tell you which key point(s) to use. Read this again if you need to.

Follow the working through carefully, making sure you understand each stage. The margin notes give useful information – make sure you read them.

Using the revision exercises

Tackle the revision exercises in the same way as the worked examples. If you need to, go back to the key points and worked examples to see which method to use.

If you are not sure what to do, look at the answer at the back of the book to see if this gives you a clue. (For example – units such as £, or a % sign will give you a hint.)

Set out your answers in a similar way to the worked examples, showing all the stages in your working. In an examination you can gain marks by doing this. If the examiner sees that you have the right method you may gain marks even if you make an error in a calculation.

Taking the practice exam

The Foundation GSCE papers are one and a half hours long, so put aside one and a half hours when you know you will not be disturbed and try to do the practice exam all in one go. This will give you some idea of how you need to pace yourself when you do the real thing.

Usually the easier topics come first in the exam, so most people start at the beginning to gain confidence by answering questions successfully.

Also, you may have some favourite topics you want to get under your belt first, so look through the whole paper at the start to get a feel for all the questions to be covered.

Wherever you start, **read the questions carefully**. Many candidates lose marks because they haven't done this.

As for the revision exercises, show all the stages in your working. If a question has 4 marks then 1 or 2 of them will be for the answer and the rest for the method you have used.

After finishing the practice exam, check your answers. If an answer is incorrect, check through your method making sure you haven't made any errors in your working.

If you can't find your mistake, use the cross reference by each question as a guide to see what to review. If you still can't find your mistake, ask your teacher to help you.

Cross references in *italic* refer to the old edition of the textbook. Cross references in roman refer to the new edition.

| What to review |

If your answer is incorrect:
review in the Foundation book:

Unit 4, page 70
Unit 4, page 75

Which edition am I using?

The new editions of the *Edexcel GCSE Maths* core textbooks have yellow cover flashes saying "ideal for the 2001 specification". You can also use the old edition (no yellow cover flash) to help you prepare for your exam.

1 Place value, approximations and estimates

Key points to remember

1 Digits can have face value and place value, for example: in 3486 the digit 4 has a face value of 4 and it has a place value of 400.

2 Numbers can be written in words, for example: 287 is two hundred and eighty seven.

3 Numbers can be written in figures, for example: two thousand and seventeen is 2017.

4 Numbers can be listed in order of size, for example: these three numbers are in order, starting with the smallest   27,   207,   270.

5 When solving number problems decide whether to add, subtract, multiply or divide.
Remember: **sum** means add, **product** means multiply, **difference** means subtract, **share** means divide.

6 Numbers can be approximated by rounding up or down.
To round to the nearest 10:
look at the digit in the units column.

- If it is less than 5 round down.
- If it is 5 or more round up.

For example:

638 rounds up to 640 as the digit in the units column is 5 or more.
Note: To round to the nearest 100, look at the digit in the tens column. To round to the nearest 1000, look at the digit in the hundreds column.

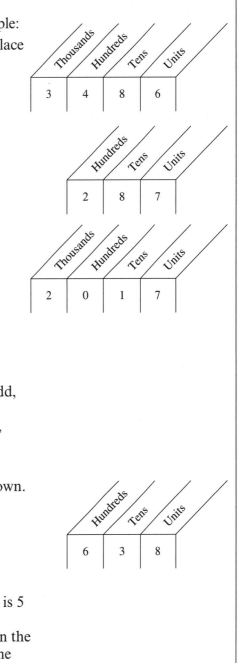

7   To write a number to 1 significant figure, look at the place value of the first digit and round the number to this place value.

8   Rounding is used to help you estimate an answer, for example:

372×23 can be estimated by
$400 \times 20 = 8000$

You can check your estimate using a calculator.
$372 \times 23 = 8556$

Example 1

(a)   The attendance at a concert was two thousand six hundred and five.
Write this number in figures.

(b)   Write the number 12 037 in words.

Answer

(a)   Using **1** and **3**, two thousand six hundred and five can be displayed as

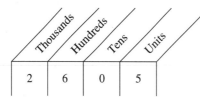

so, in figures it is written as 2605.

(b)   Using **1** and **2**, 12 037 is displayed as

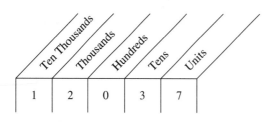

so it is

one ten thousand ⎫
two thousands   ⎬ twelve thousand
no hundreds   nothing spoken or written
three tens   ⎫
seven units   ⎬ thirty seven

So in words it is twelve thousand and thirty seven.

Worked examination question 1 [E]

There are three cards with numbers on.
The cards are placed to make the number 419.

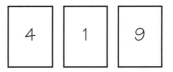

(a) Rearrange the cards to give:
    (i) the largest number possible
    (ii) the smallest number possible.

One extra card would be needed to make the number 419 ten times bigger.

(b) What extra card would you need to add?

Answer

(a) (i) Using **4** the largest number is 941.

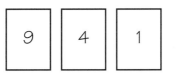

    (ii) Using **4** the smallest number is 149.

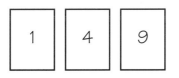

(b) Using **1** 419 can be displayed as

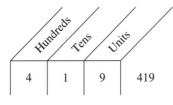

and multiplying by ten moves each of the digits one place to the left

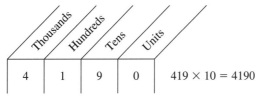

so the extra card should be

Example 2

Without using a calculator work out:

(a) 317×23 (b) $912 \div 34$

Answer

(a) $317 \times 23 = $ 317

$$\begin{array}{r} 317 \\ 23 \times \\ \hline 951 \\ 6340 + \\ \hline 7291 \\ \hline \end{array}$$

multiplying by the units figure 3 gives 951

putting a zero in the units column and multiplying by the tens figure 2 gives 6340 (this is the same as multiplying by 20)

adding 951 and 6340 gives the result of multiplying by 3 + 20 = 23

So $317 \times 23 = 7291$

(b) $912 \div 34$

34 goes into 91   34 goes into 232
2 times remainder 23   6 times remainder 28

$$\begin{array}{r} 2 \\ 34\overline{)912} \\ 68 \ - \\ \hline 23 \end{array}$$

$$\begin{array}{r} 26 \\ 34\overline{)912} \\ 68\downarrow \\ \hline 232 - \\ 204 \\ \hline 28 \end{array}$$

$1 \times 34 = 34$
$2 \times 34 = 68$
$3 \times 34 = 102$
$4 \times 34 = 136$
$5 \times 34 = 170$
$6 \times 34 = 204$
$7 \times 34 = 238$

So $912 \div 34 = 26$ remainder 28
$= 26\frac{28}{34}$.

Worked examination question 2 [E]

A small glass holds $85 \, \text{cm}^3$ of liquid. A bottle holds $2000 \, \text{cm}^3$ of liquid.
(a)   Work out the number of $85 \, \text{cm}^3$ glasses which can be filled from the bottle.
(b)   Work out the amount of liquid left in the bottle when the glasses have been filled.

85 cm³   2000 cm³

Answer

(a)   Using **5**
      we want $2000 \div 85$
      $2000 \div 85 = 23.52\ldots$
      so we could fill 23 small glasses.

Do not round up to 24 glasses as the last glass will not be full.

(b)   Using **5**
      $23 \times 85 = 1955$
      so the amount left over is
      $$2000 - 1955 = 45 \, \text{cm}^3$$

Example 3

Katie wants to work out

$$48 \times 317$$

on her calculator.

(a) Write down two approximations she could use to help estimate the answer.
(b) Work out her estimate using these approximations.
(c) Using your calculator, work out the difference between the estimate and the exact answer.

Answer

(a) Using **7**

8 is greater than 5, so round 48 up to 50.
1 is less than 5, so round 317 down to 300.

(b) Using **8**

$50 \times 300 = 15\,000$

so the estimate is 15 000

(c) Using **8**, and by calculator,

$48 \times 317 = 15\,216$

so the difference between the estimate and the exact number is
$15\,216 - 15\,000 = 216$

You could use other approximations, for instance, 317 could be approximated as 320.

Revision exercise 1

1 Minal has thrown three dice: the numbers 2, 5 and 3 are shown on the faces.
   (a) Write down the largest three-digit number that Minal can make using these three numbers.
   (b) Write down the smallest three-digit number that Minal can make using these three numbers. [E]

2 In a cycling expedition, team A and team B each have to cycle a distance of 100 kilometres in three days.
   (a) On the first two days team A cycles 29 and 35 kilometres respectively. How far must team A cycle on the third day?
   (b) Team B cycles 25 kilometres on the first day. How far could team B cycle on days two and three to reach a total of 100 kilometres in three days.

3 The number of people at a football match was 8681.
   Write down 8681 correct to the nearest one hundred. [E]

4 In this question you must show **all** your working.
   Without using a calculator work out 148×23. [E]

5 Tickets for a concert cost £3 each. Ramana has £17.
Work out the greatest number of tickets that Ramana can buy.
[E]

6 The winning numbers in the National Lottery one week were

> 49   36   46   39   23   7

Write the numbers in order of size.
Put the smallest one first.
[E]

7 247 pupils and 13 teachers are going on a school visit by coach.
Each coach holds 55 passengers.
(a) How many coaches are needed?
Each coach costs £157.50 to hire.
(b) How much will the coaches cost altogether?
[E]

8 A pupil was asked to take 230 away from 670 and gave the answer 900.
(a) Explain why this answer cannot be correct.
(b) Explain what you think the pupil did to get the answer 900.

9 (a) Write down two numbers you could use to get an approximate answer to

> 41×89

(b) Work out your approximate answer.
(c) Work out the difference between your approximate answer and the exact answer.
[E]

10 In this question do **not** use a calculator and show **all** your working.
Calculate:
(a) 256×37
(b) $954 \div 37$
[E]

11 A row of 8 CDs measured 88 mm. James is designing a shelf to hold his CDs.

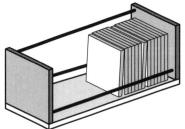

The shelf is 500 mm long. How many CDs will it hold?   [E]

12 In each part of this question write down simple approximations for each number and use them to find an estimate for each calculation.
(a) 471×87
(b) $1981 \div 369$

Test yourself	**What to review**

If your answer is incorrect, review Foundation book:

1 (a) Write the number six thousand and twelve in figures.

Unit 1, Section 1.2
Unit 1, Section 1.2

(b) In its first week a record sold 51 207 copies.
Write this number in words.

Unit 1, Section 1.2
Unit 1, Section 1.2

(c)

71
701
1070   710
107   17

Write the numbers in the cloud in order.
Start with the smallest.

Unit 1, Section 1.2
Unit 1, Section 1.2

2 You **must not** use a calculator for this question.
Show **all** your working
There are 24 hours in a day.
(a) Work out the number of hours in 365 days.

Unit 1, Section 1.3
Unit 1, Section 1.3

(b) Work out how many days are equal to 864 hours.

Unit 1, Section 1.3
Unit 1, Section 1.3

3 Lester wishes to work out 399×21 on his calculator.
Before doing so, he decides to find an estimate of the answer.
(a) Write down two numbers he could use to get an estimated
answer.

Unit 1, Section 1.5
Unit 1, Section 1.5

(b) Work out the estimate.

Unit 1, Example 5
Unit 1, Examples 7 and 8

(c) Work out the difference between the exact answer and the
estimated answer.

Unit 1, Example 6
Unit 1, Example 8

(d) Work out:
  (i) an estimate for the answer to $399 \div 21$
  (ii) the difference between your estimate and the exact
     answer.

Unit 1, pages 12–15
Unit 1, pages 17–19

Answers to Test yourself

1 (a) 6012   **(b)** Fifty one thousand, two hundred and seven.   **(c)** 17, 71, 107, 701, 710, 1070.   **2 (a)** 8760   **(b)** 36
3 (a) 400×20 **(b)** 8000   **(c)** 379   **(d)** (i) 20   (ii) 1

2 Multiples, factors and indices

Key points to remember

1 Even numbers all divide exactly by 2:   2, 4, 6, 8, . . .
Odd numbers do not divide exactly by 2:   1, 3, 5, 7, . . .
Prime numbers only divide exactly by two numbers –
themselves and 1:   2, 3, 5, 7, 11, . . .
(The number 1 is **not** a prime number because it can only
be divided by one number – itself.)

2 A factor is a whole number which will divide into another
whole number without a remainder, for example:
5 is a factor of 30 because $30 \div 5 = 6$ (whole number)
All the factors of 30 are 1, 2, 3, 5, 6, 10, 15, 30.

3 Multiples of a number are made by multiplying that
number by whole numbers, for example:
15 is a multiple of 5 because $15 = 5 \times 3$
Multiples of 5 are 5, 10, 15, 20, . . . (the 5 times table)

4 A square number is the result of multiplying one number
by itself, for example:
9 is a square number because $3 \times 3 = 9 = 3^2$ (three
squared)

5 A cube number is the result of multiplying one number
by itself, then multiplying by the number again, for
example:
8 is a cube number because $2 \times 2 \times 2 = 8 = 2^3$ (two cubed)

6 The square root of a number is the number that
multiplied by itself gives that number, for example:
$5 \times 5 = 25$ so $5 = \sqrt{25}$ (5 is the square root of 25)

7 An index number shows how many times a number is
multiplied by itself, for example:
$3^4 = 3 \times 3 \times 3 \times 3 = 81$
4 is the index or power of 3

9 dots can be arranged
as a 3 by 3 square

Example 1
(a)   List, in pairs, all the factors of 24.
(b)   Write down the factors of 24 which are
    (i)   even
    (ii) multiples of 3
    (iii) prime.

Answer

(a)   Using **2** the factors of 24 are

$$24 = 1 \times 24$$
$$= 2 \times 12$$
$$= 3 \times 8$$
$$= 4 \times 6$$

(b)   (i)   Using **2** and **1** the factors of 24 are

1, 2, 3, 4, 6, 8, 12, 24

Of these the ones which are even are

2, 4, 6, 8, 12, 24.

     (ii)   Using **3** the factors of 24 which are multiples of 3 are

3, 6, 12, 24

     (iii)   Using **1** the factors of 24 which are prime are

2 and 3 only.

Worked examination question [E]

These diagrams represent the first three square numbers.

First	Second	Third
•	• •	• • •
	• •	• • •
		• • •
1 dot	4 dots	9 dots

So the 3rd square number is 9 because 9 dots can be arranged as a square with 3 rows and 3 columns.

(a)   (i)   Draw a diagram which represents the fourth square number.
     (ii)   What is the fourth square number?
     (iii)   Explain how you got your answer.

(b)   (i)   What is the 8th square number?
     (ii)   Write down two other square numbers.

(c)   (i)   Draw up a table of all the square numbers from the 1st to the 8th.
     (ii)   Find two square numbers which add up to another square number.

(d)   Work out another two square numbers which add up to a square number.

(e)   (i)   Explain whether or not 441 is a square number.
     (ii)   Explain whether or not 1007 is a square number.

Answer

(a) Using **4**

(i) the 4th square number diagram is

```
•    •    •    •

•    •    •    •

•    •    •    •

•    •    •    •
```

(ii) the 4th square number is 16.

(iii) $4^2 = 4 \times 4 = 16$

(b) Using **4**

(i) $8^2 = 8 \times 8 = 64$

(ii) $5 \times 5 = 25$ and $6 \times 6 = 36$

(c) Using **4**

(i) the table is

Number	Square
1	1
2	4
3	9
4	16
5	25
6	36
7	49
8	64

(ii) $(3 \times 3) + (4 \times 4) = 9 + 16 = 25 = (5 \times 5)$

(d) Using **4**

$$(6 \times 6) + (8 \times 8) = 36 + 64 = 100 = (10 \times 10)$$

(e) Using **6**

(i) $\sqrt{441} = 21$ (a whole number)

so 441 **is** a square number.

(ii) $\sqrt{1007} = 31.733\ldots$ (not a whole number)

so 1007 **is not** a square number.

Example 2

(a) Work out the 4th cube number.

(b) Which is the greater, 3^4 or 4^3 and by how much?

Answer

(a) Using **5**,

4th cube number $= 4 \times 4 \times 4 = 64$.

(b) Using **7**,

$3^4 = 3 \times 3 \times 3 \times 3 = 81$ $4^3 = 4 \times 4 \times 4 = 64$

so 3^4 is the greater by $81 - 64 = 17$.

Revision exercise 2

1 Write down two different pairs of numbers that multiply together to make 32.

$$...... \times ...... = 32$$
$$...... \times ...... = 32$$

2 This number square has some numbers missing.

1	2	3	4	5	6	7	8	9	10
2	4	6	8	10	12	14	16	18	20
3	6	9	12	15	18	21	24	27	30
4	8	12	16	20	24	28	32	36	40
5	10	15	20	25	30	35	40	45	50
6	12	18	......	30	36	42	48	54	60
7	14	......	......	......	42	49	56	63	70
8	16	24	......	40	48	56	64	72	80
9	18	27	36	45	54	63	72	81	90
10	20	30	40	50	60	70	80	90	100

(a) Write down the missing numbers.
(b) Describe the number pattern in the shaded column.   [E]

3 This question is about the numbers in the box on the right.
(a) Write down the numbers which are factors of 36.
(b) Work out the sum of the two square numbers.

```
   3    5       14

 12       9     4
```

4 The factors of 10 are 10, 5, 2 and 1.
(a) Write down the factors of 15.
(b) Write down the factors of 20.
(c) Write down the largest number which is a factor of both 15 and 20.   [E]

5 Write down three multiplication sums, each of which has an answer equal to 30.
Do not use any number more than once.   [E]

6 This question is about the ten numbers in the box on the right.
(a) Write down all the numbers that divide **exactly**
    (i) by 2   (ii) by 5   (iii) by 10.
(b) Explain how you picked out the numbers in (a)(i), (ii) and (iii).
(c) Explain how you know when numbers divide exactly by 2 **and** 5 **and** 10.   [E]

```
 9010      68          764
 85      390     71
                     253
 105       437   829
```

7 Write down the next two prime numbers greater than 13.   [E]

Test yourself	**What to review**

If your answer is incorrect,
review Foundation book:

1 This question is about the numbers in the triangular box.

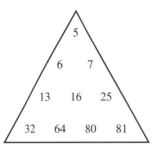

(a) Write down all the even numbers. *Unit 1, Section 1.6*
Unit 1, Section 1.6

(b) Write down all the numbers which are multiples of 5. *Unit 1, Section 1.7*
Unit 1, Section 1.7

(c) Write down the factors of 48. *Unit 1, Section 1.7*
Unit 1, Section 1.7

(d) Write down the numbers which are square numbers. *Unit 1, Section 1.8*
Unit 1, Section 1.8

(e) Write down the square root of the largest number in the box. *Unit 1, Section 1.8*
Unit 1, Section 1.8

(f) Write down the cube number. *Unit 1, Section 1.8*
Unit 1, Section 1.8

(g) Write down the sum of the three prime numbers in the box. *Unit 1, Section 1.6*
Unit 1, Section 1.6

(h) Which of the numbers in the box can be written as 2^5? *Unit 2, Section 2.7*
Unit 1, Section 1.9

2 Work out the value of $4 \times 10^3 - 4^3$. *Unit 2, Section 2.7*
Unit 1, Section 1.9

Test yourself answers

1 (a) 6, 16, 32, 64, 80 (b) 5, 25, 80 (c) 6, 16 (d) 16, 25, 64, 81 (e) 9 (f) 64 (g) 25 (h) 32   **2** 3936

3 Negative numbers

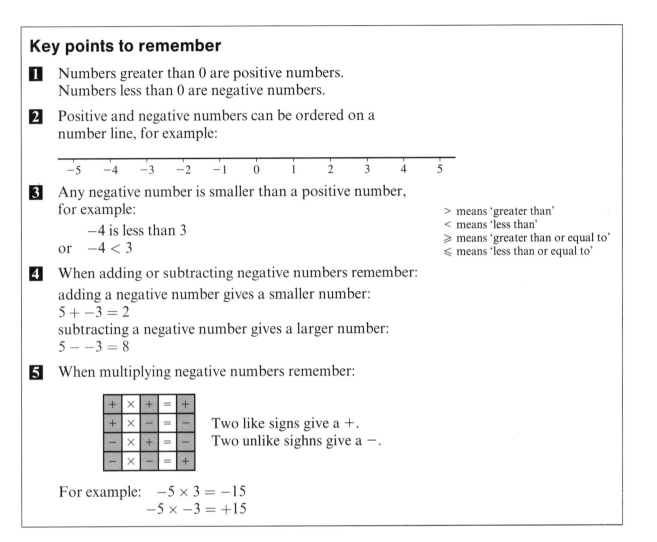

Key points to remember

1 Numbers greater than 0 are positive numbers.
Numbers less than 0 are negative numbers.

2 Positive and negative numbers can be ordered on a
number line, for example:

$$-5 \quad -4 \quad -3 \quad -2 \quad -1 \quad 0 \quad 1 \quad 2 \quad 3 \quad 4 \quad 5$$

3 Any negative number is smaller than a positive number,
for example:

    -4 is less than 3

or $-4 < 3$

> means 'greater than'
< means 'less than'
⩾ means 'greater than or equal to'
⩽ means 'less than or equal to'

4 When adding or subtracting negative numbers remember:

adding a negative number gives a smaller number:
$5 + -3 = 2$
subtracting a negative number gives a larger number:
$5 - -3 = 8$

5 When multiplying negative numbers remember:

$+$	$\times$	$+$	$=$	$+$
$+$	$\times$	$-$	$=$	$-$
$-$	$\times$	$+$	$=$	$-$
$-$	$\times$	$-$	$=$	$+$

Two like signs give a $+$.
Two unlike sighns give a $-$.

For example: $-5 \times 3 = -15$
                    $-5 \times -3 = +15$

Example 1

(a) Label the missing numbers on the number line.

$$\ldots \quad \ldots \quad -3 \quad \ldots \quad -1 \quad 0 \quad 1 \quad 2 \quad \ldots \quad 4$$

(b) Fill in 'is greater than' or 'is less than' in the following:
  (i) $4 \ldots\ldots\ldots -2$
  (ii) $-1 \ldots\ldots\ldots 0$
  (iii) $-3 \ldots\ldots\ldots -4$

Answer

(a) Using **2**,
the correct labelling is

$$-4 \quad -3 \quad -2 \quad -1 \quad 0 \quad 1 \quad 2 \quad 3 \quad 4$$

(b) Using **2** and **3**,
   (i)   4 is greater than -2
   (ii) -1 is less than 0
   (iii) -3 is greater than -4

Worked examination question 1 [E]

The lowest midnight temperatures recorded in Bradford on the days of one week were:

Day	Sun	Mon	Tues	Wed	Thur	Fri	Sat
Temp °C	8	-6	-2	0	3	-5	1

(a) Starting with the lowest, write these numbers in order.
(b) Work out the difference between the highest and lowest of these temperatures.

Answer

(a) Using **3**,
   the order is
$$-6, -5, -2, 0, 1, 3, 8.$$
(b) Using **4**,
   the difference between highest and lowest is
$$8 - (-6) = 8 + 6 = 14°C$$

Worked examination question 2 [E]

The temperature at noon was 5°C.
By 9 pm the temperature had fallen by 8°C.
Work out the temperature at 9 pm.

Answer

Using **4**, the temperature at 9 pm was
$$5 - 8 = -3°C$$

Example 2

Find, **without** using a calculator:
(a) $6 - 2 \times (-4)$
(b) $(-3)^2$

Answer

Using **5**
(a) $6 - 2 \times (-4) = 6 - (2 \times -4)$
$$= 6 - (-8)$$
$$= 6 + 8$$
$$= 14$$
(b) $(-3)^2 = (-3) \times (-3) \qquad (- \times - = +)$
$$= 9$$

Revision exercise 3

1 Here is a list of numbers.

$$-7, -2, -6, -1, -4, -9, -5, 0.$$

(a) Which is the largest of these numbers?

(b) Which is the smallest of these numbers?

2 Write the numbers in the cloud on the right in order.
Start with the smallest.

4   1
−3   −2
−7   −5

3 At midnight one day, the temperature in Leeds was −2°C.
By noon the next day, the temperature had risen by 9°C.
Work out the temperature at noon on that day in Leeds.

4 On the 27th December 1996, the maximum and minimum
recorded temperatures in Northern Ireland were

maximum   3°C
minimum   −2°C

What was the difference between the maximum and minimum
recorded temperatures in Northern Ireland that day?

5 The diagram shows part of a thermometer scale.

```
├──  15 °C
├──  10 °C
├──   5 °C
├──   0 °C
├──  −5 °C
├── −10 °C
```

Copy the scale and mark the temperature of −7°C.

6 Write down the number which is
(a) 7 less than 2
(b) 8 more than −2.

7 The temperature in London at 2 am was −3°C.
At midday the temperature had risen by 11°C.
What was the midday temperature?

8 Fill in the missing numbers.
(a) $-2 \times 10 = \ldots$
(b) $-3 \times \ldots = 21$
(c) $-15 \times -3 = \ldots$
(d) $-14 \times \ldots = -42$

9 One Autumn morning the temperature went up from $-4°C$ to $5°C$.

(a) By how many degrees did the temperature rise?

During the afternoon the temperature then fell by seven degrees from $5°C$.

(b) What was the temperature at the end of the afternoon?   [E]

10 The temperature at 6 am was $-3°C$.
At noon it had gone up by 8 degrees.

(a) What was the temperature at noon?

At 4 pm the temperature had gone down by 10 degrees from the temperature at noon.

(b) What was the temperature at 4 pm?   [E]

Test yourself	**What to review**
	If your answer is incorrect, review Foundation book:
1 Write these six numbers in order, starting with the smallest $3, -5, 2, -3, 0, -1.$	*Unit 1, pages 19–21* Unit 1, pages 24–25
2 On 1st January the maximum temperature in Derby was $5°C$. On the same day, the minimum temperature in Derby was $8°C$ below the maximum temperature. Work out the minimum temperature in Derby on that day.	*Unit 1, Section 1.9* Unit 1, Section 1.10
3 Work out **(a)** $8 - 3(-4)$ **(b)** $(-5)^2$	*Unit 1, Worked example 2* Unit 1, pages 26–27 *Unit 1, Worked example 2* Unit 1, pages 26–27

Test yourself answers

1 $-5, -3, -1, 0, 2, 3$ **2** $-3°C$ **3 (a)** 20   **(b)** 25

4 Fractions

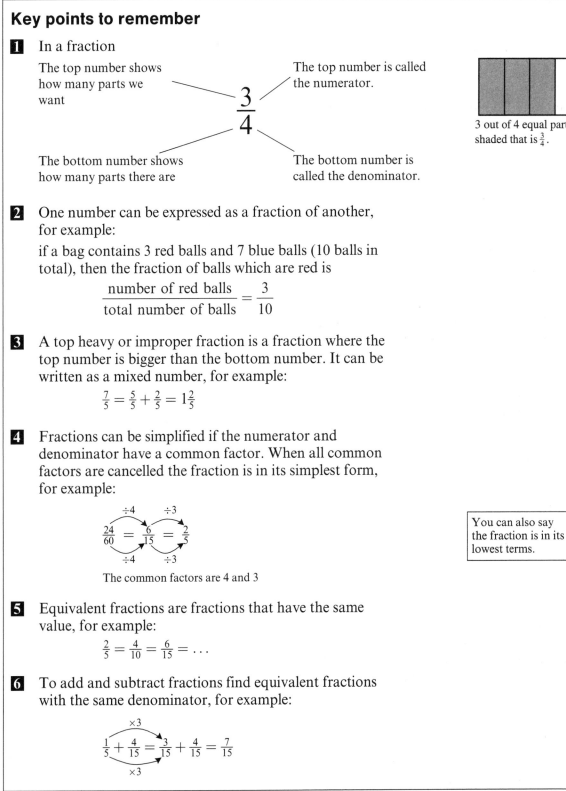

Key points to remember

1 In a fraction

The top number shows how many parts we want

The top number is called the numerator.

$$\frac{3}{4}$$

The bottom number shows how many parts there are

The bottom number is called the denominator.

3 out of 4 equal parts are shaded that is $\frac{3}{4}$.

2 One number can be expressed as a fraction of another, for example:

if a bag contains 3 red balls and 7 blue balls (10 balls in total), then the fraction of balls which are red is

$$\frac{\text{number of red balls}}{\text{total number of balls}} = \frac{3}{10}$$

3 A top heavy or improper fraction is a fraction where the top number is bigger than the bottom number. It can be written as a mixed number, for example:

$$\frac{7}{5} = \frac{5}{5} + \frac{2}{5} = 1\frac{2}{5}$$

4 Fractions can be simplified if the numerator and denominator have a common factor. When all common factors are cancelled the fraction is in its simplest form, for example:

$$\overset{\div 4}{\overset{\frown}{\frac{24}{60}}} = \overset{\div 3}{\overset{\frown}{\frac{6}{15}}} = \frac{2}{5}$$

$$\underset{\div 4}{\underset{\smile}{}} \quad \underset{\div 3}{\underset{\smile}{}}$$

The common factors are 4 and 3

You can also say the fraction is in its lowest terms.

5 Equivalent fractions are fractions that have the same value, for example:

$$\frac{2}{5} = \frac{4}{10} = \frac{6}{15} = \cdots$$

6 To add and subtract fractions find equivalent fractions with the same denominator, for example:

$$\overset{\times 3}{\overset{\frown}{\frac{1}{5}}} + \frac{4}{15} = \underset{\times 3}{\underset{\smile}{\frac{3}{15}}} + \frac{4}{15} = \frac{7}{15}$$

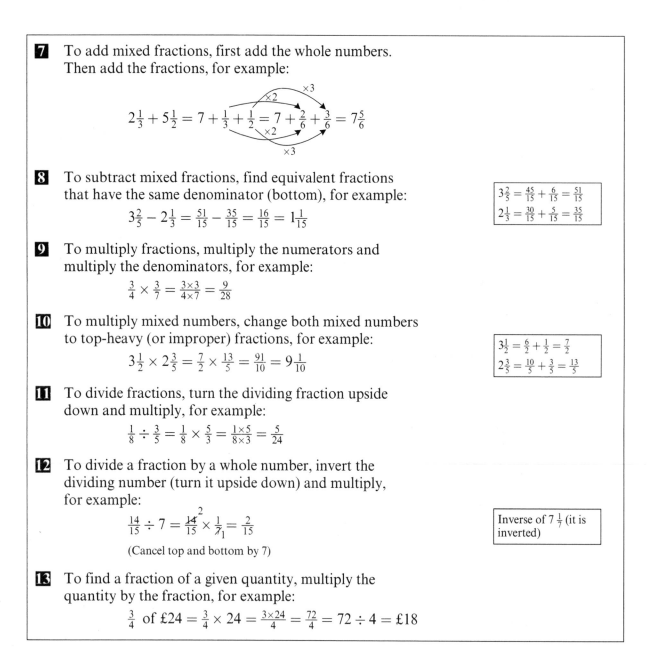

7 To add mixed fractions, first add the whole numbers.
Then add the fractions, for example:

$$2\tfrac{1}{3} + 5\tfrac{1}{2} = 7 + \tfrac{1}{3} + \tfrac{1}{2} = 7 + \tfrac{2}{6} + \tfrac{3}{6} = 7\tfrac{5}{6}$$

8 To subtract mixed fractions, find equivalent fractions
that have the same denominator (bottom), for example:

$$3\tfrac{2}{5} - 2\tfrac{1}{3} = \tfrac{51}{15} - \tfrac{35}{15} = \tfrac{16}{15} = 1\tfrac{1}{15}$$

$$3\tfrac{2}{5} = \tfrac{45}{15} + \tfrac{6}{15} = \tfrac{51}{15}$$
$$2\tfrac{1}{3} = \tfrac{30}{15} + \tfrac{5}{15} = \tfrac{35}{15}$$

9 To multiply fractions, multiply the numerators and
multiply the denominators, for example:

$$\tfrac{3}{4} \times \tfrac{3}{7} = \tfrac{3 \times 3}{4 \times 7} = \tfrac{9}{28}$$

10 To multiply mixed numbers, change both mixed numbers
to top-heavy (or improper) fractions, for example:

$$3\tfrac{1}{2} \times 2\tfrac{3}{5} = \tfrac{7}{2} \times \tfrac{13}{5} = \tfrac{91}{10} = 9\tfrac{1}{10}$$

$$3\tfrac{1}{2} = \tfrac{6}{2} + \tfrac{1}{2} = \tfrac{7}{2}$$
$$2\tfrac{3}{5} = \tfrac{10}{5} + \tfrac{3}{5} = \tfrac{13}{5}$$

11 To divide fractions, turn the dividing fraction upside
down and multiply, for example:

$$\tfrac{1}{8} \div \tfrac{3}{5} = \tfrac{1}{8} \times \tfrac{5}{3} = \tfrac{1 \times 5}{8 \times 3} = \tfrac{5}{24}$$

12 To divide a fraction by a whole number, invert the
dividing number (turn it upside down) and multiply,
for example:

$$\tfrac{14}{15} \div 7 = \tfrac{\overset{2}{14}}{15} \times \tfrac{1}{\underset{1}{7}} = \tfrac{2}{15}$$

(Cancel top and bottom by 7)

Inverse of $7\tfrac{1}{7}$ (it is
inverted)

13 To find a fraction of a given quantity, multiply the
quantity by the fraction, for example:

$$\tfrac{3}{4} \text{ of } £24 = \tfrac{3}{4} \times 24 = \tfrac{3 \times 24}{4} = \tfrac{72}{4} = 72 \div 4 = £18$$

Example 1

Richard wins £120 in a competition.
He saves £80 of this money.
Work out the amount he saves as a fraction of the amount he wins.
Express your fraction in its lowest terms.

Answer

Using **2**, the fraction is

$$\frac{\text{the amount he saves}}{\text{the amount he wins}} = \frac{80}{120}$$

Now, using **4** and **5**,

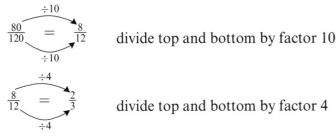

$$\frac{80}{120} = \frac{8}{12} \quad \text{÷10}$$ divide top and bottom by factor 10

$$\frac{8}{12} = \frac{2}{3} \quad \text{÷4}$$ divide top and bottom by factor 4

No more cancelling can be done.
So $\frac{80}{120}$ in its lowest terms is $\frac{2}{3}$.

Example 2

Work out:
(a) $\frac{3}{4} + \frac{1}{3}$
(b) $2\frac{5}{6} - 1\frac{1}{2}$
(c) $\frac{4}{7} \times \frac{5}{9}$
(d) $2\frac{1}{4} \div 3\frac{1}{2}$

Answer

(a) Using **6** $\frac{3}{4} + \frac{1}{3}$

turn both into equivalent fractions of $\frac{1}{12}$:

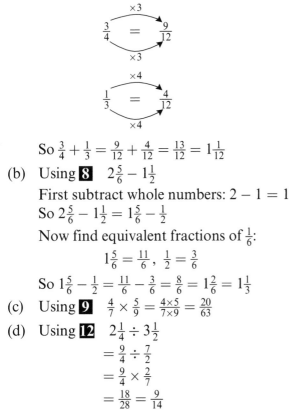

$$\frac{3}{4} = \frac{9}{12}$$

$$\frac{1}{3} = \frac{4}{12}$$

So $\frac{3}{4} + \frac{1}{3} = \frac{9}{12} + \frac{4}{12} = \frac{13}{12} = 1\frac{1}{12}$

(b) Using **8** $2\frac{5}{6} - 1\frac{1}{2}$

First subtract whole numbers: $2 - 1 = 1$
So $2\frac{5}{6} - 1\frac{1}{2} = 1\frac{5}{6} - \frac{1}{2}$
Now find equivalent fractions of $\frac{1}{6}$:

$$1\frac{5}{6} = \frac{11}{6}, \ \frac{1}{2} = \frac{3}{6}$$

So $1\frac{5}{6} - \frac{1}{2} = \frac{11}{6} - \frac{3}{6} = \frac{8}{6} = 1\frac{2}{6} = 1\frac{1}{3}$

(c) Using **9** $\frac{4}{7} \times \frac{5}{9} = \frac{4 \times 5}{7 \times 9} = \frac{20}{63}$

(d) Using **12** $2\frac{1}{4} \div 3\frac{1}{2}$

$$= \frac{9}{4} \div \frac{7}{2}$$
$$= \frac{9}{4} \times \frac{2}{7}$$
$$= \frac{18}{28} = \frac{9}{14}$$

> make them both top
> heavy fractions

Worked examination question 1 [E]

(a)   Shade $\frac{3}{5}$ of the rectangle below.

(b)   What fraction of the strip is marked A?

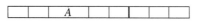

(c)   At the start of a game of snooker there is a total of 21 balls on the table.
15 of these balls are red.
Express the number of red balls as a fraction of the total number of balls.
Write the fraction in its lowest terms.

Answer

(a)   Using **1**, $\frac{3}{5}$ of the rectangle is

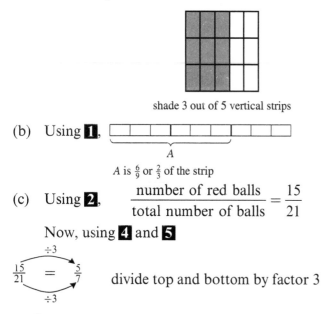

shade 3 out of 5 vertical strips

(b)   Using **1**,

A is $\frac{6}{9}$ or $\frac{2}{3}$ of the strip

(c)   Using **2**, $\dfrac{\text{number of red balls}}{\text{total number of balls}} = \dfrac{15}{21}$

Now, using **4** and **5**

$$\frac{15}{21} = \frac{5}{7} \qquad \div 3$$

divide top and bottom by factor 3

So $\frac{5}{7}$ of the balls are red

Worked examination question 2 [E]

Wesley's salary is £14 000 each year.
He pays $\frac{2}{7}$ of his salary in income tax and national insurance contributions each year.
Work out the amount Wesley pays in income tax and national insurance each year.

Answer

Using **13**,

$$\frac{2}{7} \text{ of } £14\,000 = \frac{2}{7} \times 14\,000$$

$$= \frac{2 \times 14\,000}{7} = \frac{28\,000}{7} = 4000$$

So Wesley pays £4000 each year in income tax and national insurance contributions.

Revision exercise 4

1 Work out:
   (a) $\frac{1}{2} + \frac{1}{5}$
   (b) $2\frac{1}{3} + 3\frac{1}{4}$
   (c) $\frac{2}{3} - \frac{1}{4}$
   (d) $4\frac{1}{5} - \frac{1}{10}$
   (e) $4\frac{7}{8} - 3\frac{3}{4}$
   (f) $\frac{3}{5} \times \frac{2}{3}$
   (g) $\frac{3}{5} \times 9$
   (h) $1\frac{3}{5} \times 2\frac{2}{3}$
   (i) $\frac{1}{2} \div \frac{3}{4}$
   (j) $\frac{5}{8} \div 7$
   (k) $2\frac{3}{10} \times 3$
   (l) $3\frac{1}{6} \div 1\frac{7}{8}$

2 An election was held in which 330 votes were cast.
   One third of the votes was for Bertie.
   How many votes was this? [E]

3 At the start of the year Fatima had £240 in her bank account.
   At the end of the year she had £312 in her bank account.
   Work out the increase in her bank account as a fraction, in its lowest terms, of the amount in her bank account at the start of the year. [E]

4 There are 570 people at a concert.
   $\frac{2}{3}$ of these people are female.
   Work out the number of females at the concert.

5 The normal price of a ticket is £5.40.
   As a special offer, there is $\frac{1}{3}$ off the price.
   Work out the special offer price. [E]

6 1 kilometre $= \frac{5}{8}$ of a mile.
   Convert 24 kilometres to miles.

7 Work out, in minutes
   (a) $\frac{1}{4}$ of an hour
   (b) $\frac{2}{5}$ of an hour.

   Remember
   1 hour = 60 minutes

8 What fraction of an hour is
   (a) 45 minutes
   (b) 40 minutes?
   Give your answers in their simplest forms.

9 Janet wishes to buy a motor cycle on hire purchase.
The cost of the motor cycle is £1650.
Janet must pay a deposit of $\frac{1}{4}$ of the cost price of the motor cycle.
Work out the deposit Janet must pay.

10 At the start of a game there are 24 coloured balls on a table.
15 of these balls are red. What fraction of the coloured balls are
(a) red   **(b)** not red.
Give your answers in their simplest terms.

11 Barbara's wages are £230 per week this year.
For next year she has been promised a rise of $\frac{1}{5}$ of her wages
this year.
Work out when Barbara's wages, per weeks, should be next year.

12 Using the list of prices opposite,
(a) Work out the cost of 5 breakfasts.

Dara buys some cups of tea.
(b) Work out the greatest number of cups of tea she can buy with £5.

A child's meal costs $\frac{7}{10}$ of the price of Today's Special.
(c) Work out the cost of a child's meal.   [E]

Sam's Cafe	
Cup of tea	80p
Cup of coffee	90p
Breakfast	£2.95
Today's Special	£4

Test yourself   What to review

If your answer is incorrect,
review Foundation book:

1 In a sale a shopkeeper reduces all prices by $\frac{1}{3}$.   *Unit 4, Section 4.5*
Before the sale, the price of a coat was £102.   Unit 4, Section 4.5
Work out the price of this coat in the sale.

2 There are 24 pupils in class 11T at Lucea High School.   *Unit 4, Sections 4.2 and 4.4*
16 of these pupils are girls.   Unit 4, Sections 4.2 and 4.4
What fraction of class 11T are girls.
Give your answer in its simplest form.

3 Work out   *Unit 4, Section 4.8*
(a) $\frac{3}{4}+\frac{5}{8}$ **(b)** $3\frac{1}{2} \div 2\frac{1}{4}$ Unit 4, Section 4.8
                    Unit 4, Section 4.11
                    Unit 4, Section 4.11

Test yourself answers

1 £68   **2** $\frac{2}{3}$ **3 (a)** $1\frac{3}{8}$ **(b)** $1\frac{4}{9}$

5 Decimals

A decimal is a way of representing a number using tenths, hundredths, thousandths, etc.

Key points to remember

1 In a decimal number the decimal point separates the whole number from the part that is smaller than 1.

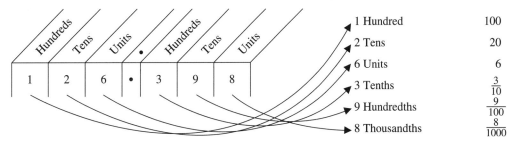

1 Hundred	100
2 Tens	20
6 Units	6
3 Tenths	$\frac{3}{10}$
9 Hundredths	$\frac{9}{100}$
8 Thousandths	$\frac{8}{1000}$

2 To round a decimal to the nearest whole number, look at the number in the tenths column. If it is 5 or more add 1 to the units (round up). If it is less than 5 do not change the units (round down).

17.6 rounds to 18.
17.4 rounds to 17.

3 Decimals can be rounded to a number of decimal places by looking at the figure to the right of the last decimal place you want. If this figure is less than 5 round down, but if it is 5 or more round up, for example:

2.837 rounds up to 2 decimal places as 2.84 (as 7 is more than 5)

5.8143 rounds down to 3 decimal places as 5.814 (as 3 is less than 5)

If you want one decimal place, look at the second decimal place (hundredths)

For two decimal places, look at the third decimal place. For three decimal places, look at the fourth decimal place.

4 When making a decimal addition or subtraction sum always put the decimal points under each other.

$$2.64 + 9.1 = \begin{array}{r} 2.64 \\ 9.1 + \\ \hline 11.74 \end{array}$$

5 When multiplying decimals the answer must have the same number of decimal places as the total number of decimal places in the numbers being multiplied.
2.3 has 1 decimal place and 3.61 has 2 decimal places.
So 2.3 × 3.61 will have 3 decimal places.

6 Fractions can be changed into decimals by dividing the numerator by the denominator.
$\frac{3}{5} = 3 \div 5 = 0.6$

7 A number can be rounded to a number of significant
figures. Count from the left of the number from the first
non-zero digit.

For example: 52367 is 52400 to 3 significant figures.
               0.00637 is 0.0064 to 2 significant figures.

8 You can sort decimal numbers in order of size by first
comparing the whole numbers, then the digits in the tenth
place, then the digits in the hundredths place, and so on.

Example 1
Petrol costs 64.9 pence a litre.
Lynn buys 24.6 litres of petrol.
Work out the cost of the petrol Lynn buys.
Give your answer in pounds and pence, correct to the nearest
penny.

Answer
Using **5**, the cost is

$$24.6 \times 64.9 = 1596.54\text{p (by calculator)}$$
$$= £15.9654$$

Using **3**, to the nearest penny, we round this number up to the 2nd
decimal place as £15.97.

Worked examination question 1 [E]
Mark with an X a point which is approximately 0.6 of the way
along the line from A.

Answer
Using **6**, the point must be

more than $\frac{1}{2}(=0.5)$ of the way along from A, and
less than $\frac{3}{4}(=0.75)$ of the way along from A
since $0.5 < 0.6 < 0.75$

So the point is approximately

Worked examination question 2 [E]

Janivir wishes to buy a TV. The cost is £360.
Janivir has saved £108 as a deposit.
Work out the deposit as a decimal of the cost of the TV.

Answer

Using **6**,
deposit as a fraction of the cost $= \frac{£108}{£360}$
Dividing to get a decimal,
deposit as a decimal of the cost $= 108 \div 360 = 0.3$

Example 2

Work out 2.78×1.3
You **must not** use a calculator.

Answer

Firstly, we work out 278×13 ignoring any decimal points.

$$
\begin{array}{r}
278 \\
\times \quad 13 \\
\hline
834 \\
2780 \\
\hline
3614
\end{array}
$$

$834 \quad (3 \times 278)$
$2780 \quad (10 \times 278)$

or $278 \times 13 = 278 \times 10 + 278 \times 3$
$= 2780 + 834$
$= 3614$

> There is more on long multiplication in Unit 1.

So $278 \times 13 = 3614$
But, using **5**, the calculation $\quad 2.78 \times 1.3$

$\qquad\qquad\qquad\qquad\qquad \uparrow \qquad \uparrow$
$\qquad\qquad\qquad 2 \text{ d.p.} + 1 \text{ d.p.} = 3 \text{ d.p. in total}$

So the answer needs 3 decimal places or 3 numbers after the decimal point.

$278 \times 13 = 3614$ means that $2.78 \times 1.3 = 3.614$

Example 3

Put these decimals in order of size, smallest first:

$\qquad\qquad 5.14, \ 15.31, \ 5.04, \ 50.04, \ 5.41$

Using **8** compare whole numbers:
$\qquad\qquad\qquad\qquad\qquad\qquad 5.14$
$\qquad\qquad\qquad\qquad\qquad\qquad 5.04$
$\qquad\qquad\qquad\qquad\qquad\qquad 5.41$
$\qquad\qquad\qquad\qquad\qquad\qquad 15.31$
$\qquad\qquad\qquad\qquad\qquad\qquad 50.04$

Then tenths place:
$\qquad\qquad\qquad\qquad\qquad\qquad 5.04$
$\qquad\qquad\qquad\qquad\qquad\qquad 5.14$
$\qquad\qquad\qquad\qquad\qquad\qquad 5.41$
$\qquad\qquad\qquad\qquad\qquad\qquad 15.31$
$\qquad\qquad\qquad\qquad\qquad\qquad 50.04$

So the order is 5.04, 5.14, 5.41, 15.31, 50.04.

Revision exercise 5

1 Write $\frac{3}{5}$ as a decimal.

2 Without using a calculator, work out
$$1.48 \times 2.3$$

3 A 5 metre length of wood is cut into 3 pieces.
One piece is 2.46 metres long.
Another piece is 86 centimetres long.
How long is the third piece of wood?

> 1 metre = 100 centimetres

4 Central heating oil costs 18.42p per litre.
Steve pays for 900 litres of central heating oil.
How much does Steve pay?
Write your answer in pounds.

5 Calculate the area, in cm², of a rectangle which measures 4.3 cm
by 5.2 cm.

> Area of rectangle = length × width

6 Write the fraction $\frac{5}{8}$ as a decimal.

7 Work out $\dfrac{2.86 \times 3.01}{1.7}$
giving your answer correct to 3 decimal places.

8 1 mile = 1.6 kilometres.
Convert 8.2 miles to kilometres.

9 Tickets for a football match cost £4.70 each.
(a) How much will 100 tickets cost?

Children can buy tickets at half price.
Mr and Mrs Smith and their two children buy tickets.
(b) Work out the total cost of the tickets.   [E]

10 Write these numbers in order, starting with the smallest.
$$0.42, \quad \frac{2}{5}, \quad \frac{43}{100}, \quad 0.402$$

> Hint: Change the fractions to decimals first.

11 Mrs Aspill pays £471.12 each calendar month for her mortgage.
Calculate her total mortgage payment for a year.
Show all your working.
You **must not** use a calculator.

Test yourself	What to review
	If your answer is incorrect, review Foundation book:

1 Jane buys 12.8 gallons of diesel.
Each gallon of diesel costs £2.768.

Work out how much Jane has to pay for her 12.8 gallons of diesel.

(a) in pounds and pence correct to the nearest penny

Unit 6, pages 89–90 and 85–86

(b) in pounds, correct to the nearest pound.

Unit 6, pages 106–107 and 102–103

2 Two children weigh 24.62 kg and 31.7 kg.
Find their combined weight.
Do not use a calculator.

Unit 6, Section 6.3
Unit 6, section 6.4

3 You must show **all** your working.
You must **not** use a calculator.
Work out $\frac{2}{5}$ of (3.8×2.7).

Unit 6, pages 89–92
Unit 6, pages 106–108

Test yourself answers

1 (a) £35.43 (b) £35   **2** 56.32 kg   **3** 4.104

6 Percentages

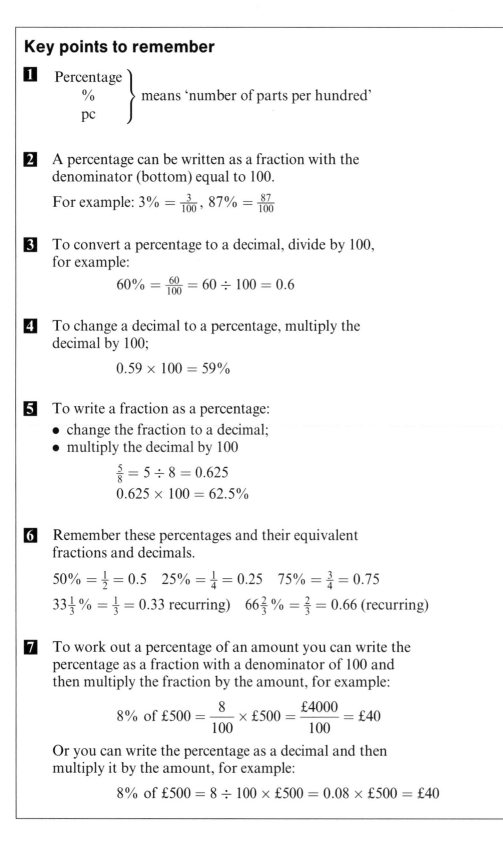

Key points to remember

1. Percentage
   %   } means 'number of parts per hundred'
   pc

2. A percentage can be written as a fraction with the denominator (bottom) equal to 100.

   For example: $3\% = \frac{3}{100}$, $87\% = \frac{87}{100}$

3. To convert a percentage to a decimal, divide by 100, for example:

   $$60\% = \frac{60}{100} = 60 \div 100 = 0.6$$

4. To change a decimal to a percentage, multiply the decimal by 100;

   $$0.59 \times 100 = 59\%$$

5. To write a fraction as a percentage:
   - change the fraction to a decimal;
   - multiply the decimal by 100

   $$\frac{5}{8} = 5 \div 8 = 0.625$$
   $$0.625 \times 100 = 62.5\%$$

6. Remember these percentages and their equivalent fractions and decimals.

   $50\% = \frac{1}{2} = 0.5$ $25\% = \frac{1}{4} = 0.25$ $75\% = \frac{3}{4} = 0.75$

   $33\frac{1}{3}\% = \frac{1}{3} = 0.33$ recurring) $66\frac{2}{3}\% = \frac{2}{3} = 0.66$ (recurring)

7. To work out a percentage of an amount you can write the percentage as a fraction with a denominator of 100 and then multiply the fraction by the amount, for example:

   $$8\% \text{ of } £500 = \frac{8}{100} \times £500 = \frac{£4000}{100} = £40$$

   Or you can write the percentage as a decimal and then multiply it by the amount, for example:

   $$8\% \text{ of } £500 = 8 \div 100 \times £500 = 0.08 \times £500 = £40$$

8 To write one amount as a percentage of a second amount:

- write the fraction $\dfrac{\text{1st amount}}{\text{2nd amount}}$
- concert the fraction to a decimal
- multiply the decimal by 100

for example:

to find £12 as a percentage of £48
fraction $= \frac{12}{48}$,   decimal $= 12 \div 48 = 0.25$,
percentage $= 0.25 \times 100\% = 25\%$.

9 To increase a quantity by a percentage, work out the actual increase and then add it to the original quantity.

To decrease a quantity by a percentage, work out the actual decrease and then subtract it from the original quantity.

Worked examination question 1 [E]
Write these numbers in order, starting with the smallest

$$63\%, \quad 0.65, \quad \tfrac{3}{5}$$

Answer

Using **3**,
change the percentage to a decimal

$$63\% = \tfrac{63}{100} = 0.63$$

Also $\frac{3}{5} = 0.6$ since $\quad 5\overline{)3.00}^{\,0.6}$

So the numbers, as decimals, are

$$0.63, \qquad 0.65, \qquad 0.6$$

0.6 is the same as 0.60

In order, starting with the smallest they are

0.6,	0.63	0.65
$\frac{3}{5}$,	63%	0.65

Worked examination question 2 [E]
At the beginning of the year Nzinga had £240 in her savings.
At the end of the year she had managed to increase her savings to £324.
Calculate the percentage increase in her savings.

Answer

The increase in Nzinga's savings is

$$£324 - £240 = £84$$

Using **8**, the increase as a fraction $= \frac{80}{240}$
$$\text{as a decimal} = 80 \div 240 = 0.35$$
$$\text{as a percentage} = 0.35 \times 100 = 35\%.$$

Worked examination question 3 [E]

In 1996 an oil company charged 15p for a litre of oil.
In 1997 the oil company increased its charge for a litre of oil by 6%.
(a)   Calculate 6% of 15p.
(b)   Work out the oil company's charge for a litre of oil in 1997.

Answer

(a)   Using **7**,
     6% of $15 = \frac{6}{100} \times 15 = 0.06 \times 15 = 0.9$p
(b)   Using **9**,
     the 1997 charge for a litre of oil is
     $15 + 0.9 = 15.9$p

Revision exercise 6

1   Work out 35% of £560.

2   Fiona bought a new car on 1st January 1994.
    The value of the car then was £12 000.
    On 1st January 1997, Fiona was told that the value of her car was 48% of its value on 1st January 1994.

    Work out the value of Fiona's car on 1st January 1997.

3   The price of a van is given below

    > Van   £3000
    > plus VAT at 17.5%

    (a) Work out 17.5% of £3000.
    (b) Work out the price of the van when VAT is added on.

4   John wants to buy a motor cycle.
    The price of the motor cycle is £2200.
    John is told that he must pay a deposit of £770.

    Work out the deposit John must pay as a percentage of the price of the motor cycle.

5 Here is a list of fractions, decimals and percentages

$$67\%, \quad \tfrac{1}{2}, \quad 0.6, \quad 25\%, \quad 0.3, \quad \tfrac{3}{8}$$

Rewrite the list in order of size, starting with the smallest first.

[E]

6 Amy and Neil go out for a meal.
The cost of the meal is £22 plus 12% service charge.
Work out the total cost of the meal when the service charge is included.

7 There are 1200 pupils at Lucea High School.
49% of the pupils at Lucea High School are male.
Work out the number of male pupils at Lucea High School.

8 Steve bought a car for £850. He sold it for £595.
Work out the percentage loss Steve made on this car.

9 Blackburn Rovers bought Alan Shearer for £3 million.
They sold him for £15 million.
Work out the percentage profit Blackburn Rovers made on Alan Shearer.

10 Dee's wages are £1200 per month.
Her taxes are £408 per month.
Work out her taxes per month as a percentage of her wages.

11 (a) Copy the rectangle and shade 40% of it.

(b) What percentage of the circle below is shaded?

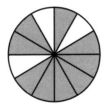

Test yourself	What to review
	If your answer is incorrect, review Foundation book:
1 Work out 40% of £65.	*Unit 14, Examples 5 and 6* Unit 14, Examples 10 and 11
2 600 000 people sit an examination. 330 000 people pass this examination. Work out, as a percentage of the people who take the examination, the number of people who pass the examination.	*Unit 14, Example 9* Unit 14, Example 14
3 Steve wants to buy a computer. The price of the computer is quoted at £1200 plus VAT at 17.5%. **(a)** Work out 17.5% of £1200.	*Unit 14, Examples 5 and 6* Unit 14, Examples 10 and 11
(b) Work out the total price, including VAT, that Steve must pay for the computer. Steve buys the computer for the total price including VAT. A year later he sells the computer for £1000.	*Unit 14, Example 7* Unit 14, Example 12
(c) Work out the loss he makes, as a percentage of the total price he paid for the computer, including VAT. Give your answer as a percentage, correct to the nearest whole number.	*Unit 14, Example 11* Unit 14, Example 15

Test yourself answers

1 £26   **2** 55%   **3 (a)** £210   **(b)** £1410   **(c)** 29%

7 Ratio and proportion

Key points to remember

1 When a quantity is split in a ratio such as 3 parts of the quantity to 2 parts of the quantity, this is written as a ratio $3:2$.

2 Ratios can be used to share or divide quantities. For example:

To share £85 in the ratio $3:2$, $3 + 2 = 5$ so 1 part; $= 85 \div 5 = £17$
so 2 parts $= 2 \times £17 = £34$
3 parts $= 3 \times £17 = £51$

3 You can simplify a ratio if you can divide both its numbers by a common factor. For example:

$6:4$ simplifies because 6 and 4 have a factor of 2.
So $\quad 6:4$
$= 6 \div 2 : 4 \div 2$
$= \quad\quad 3:2$

4 When a ratio cannot be simplified then it is said to be in its lowest terms. Ratios are usually written in their lowest terms.

5 Two quantities are in proportion if their ratio stays the same as each of the quantities get larger or smaller.

6 The unitary method is a way of solving ratio and proportion problems by finding the value of one unit of a quantity first, for example:

100 g peanuts cost $\quad$ 50p
1 g peanuts cost $\quad \frac{50}{100}$p ————— divide by 100 to find the cost of 1 g.
so 250 g peanuts cost $\quad \frac{50}{100} \times 250$p ————250 g cost 250 × the cost of 1 g.

7 A ratio called a scale is used to show the relationship between a distance on a map, diagram or model and the real distance.

Ordnance survey maps use a scale $1:50\,000$. This means 1 cm on the map represents 500 m.

Example 1

Mr Khan wins 35000 in the lottery. He keeps £1400 for himself.
He then gives the remainder of his winnings to his wife and daughter.
He divides the money he gives to his wife and daughter in the ratio $3:2$.

Calculate the amount of money Mr Khan gives to
(a)   his wife
(b)   his daughter.

Answer

Mr Khan keeps £1400 for himself.
So the amount he shares between his wife and daughter is

$$£5000 - £1400 = £3600.$$

So, using **1** and **2**, he divides £3600 in the ratio $3:2$.

总 total parts $= 3 + 2 = 5$
so one part $= £3600 \div 5 = £720$

(a)   His wife gets $3 \times £720 = £2160$
(b)   His daughter gets $2 \times £720 = £1440$

Note: It is worth checking:
£1400   + £2160 + £1440 = £5000
(Mr Khan)   (wife)   (daughter)

Worked examination question [E]

Here is a list of ingredients for making some Greek food.
These amounts make enough for 6 people.

2 cloves of garlic
4 ounces of chick peas
4 tablespoons of olive oil
5 fluid ounces of Tahini paste

Change these amounts so that there will be enough for 9 people.

Answer

Using **3** and **6**,
the ratio of people is

$6:9$
or $2:3$
or $1:1\frac{1}{2}$ $(9 = 6 \times 1\frac{1}{2})$

So we need to multiply each of the amounts by $1\frac{1}{2}$.

$2 \times 1\frac{1}{2} = 3$ cloves of garlic

$4 \times 1\frac{1}{2} = 6$ ounces of chick peas

$4 \times 1\frac{1}{2} = 6$ tablespoons of olive oil

$5 \times 1\frac{1}{2} = 7\frac{1}{2}$ fluid ounces of Tahini paste

Example 2

A road map is drawn to a scale of

$1:250\,000$

The true distance between Sheffield and Newcastle is 212
kilometres.

Work out the distance, on the map, between Sheffield and Newcastle.

Give your answer, in centimetres, correct to the nearest centimetre.

Answer

Using **7**,

distance on map in km: $212 \, \text{km} = 1 : 250\,000$

$$\text{or} \frac{\text{distance on map in km}}{212 \, \text{km}} = \frac{1}{250\,000}$$

$212 \, \text{km} = 212 \times 1000 = 212\,000 \, \text{m}$

$212\,000 \, \text{m} = 212\,000 \times 100 = 21\,200\,000 \, \text{cm}$ ——————

$$\text{So} \frac{\text{distance on map in cm}}{21\,200\,000 \, \text{cm}} = \frac{1}{250\,000}$$

so distance on map in cm $= 21\,200\,000 \times \dfrac{1}{250\,000}$

$= 84.8 \, \text{cm}$

So, correct to the nearest cm, the distance on the map is $85 \, \text{cm}$.

| $1 \, \text{km} = 1000 \, \text{m}$ |
| $1 \, \text{m} = 100 \, \text{cm}$ |

The question asks for the answer in centimetres, so change 212 km to centimetres.

Revision exercise 7

1 Ingredients (for 6 small cakes)

  12 ounces self-raising flour
   2 ounces cornflour
   6 ounces butter
   8 ounces caster sugar
   2 eggs

Sixty cakes are to be made.
  (a) Find the weight, in lb, of self-raising flour needed to make the cakes.
  (b) Change the amounts in the recipe so that there will be enough to make 15 small cakes.
  (c) Change $\frac{3}{4}$ ounces into grams.
    Give your answer correct to 1 decimal place.   [E]

| 16 ounces = 1 lb |

| 454 grams = 1 lb |

2 Fred won a prize of £12 000.
He put some of the money in a Building Society and the rest of the money in the Post Office.
The money was put in the Building Society and Post Office in the ratio $2 : 3$.
  (a) Calculate the amount of money put in the Building Society.

After a number of years the money put in the Building Society had increased by 9%.
  (b) Calculate the amount of money Fred then had in the Building Society.

After the same number of years the money Fred had put in the Post Office had increased by an eighth.

(c) Calculate the increase in the amount of money in the Post Office.   [E]

3 In a recipe for scones,
     the ratio of flour to fat is 4 : 1
   and the ratio of flour to sugar is 8 : 1.
   Complete the recipe below.

> Recipe for Scones
> 50 g of fat
> ... g flour
> ... g sugar   [E]

4 A plan is drawn on a scale of 2 cm represents 10 m.
   Write this as a ratio in the form 1 : n, where n is a whole number.   [E]

> 100 cm = 1 m

5 Members of the 'Dolphins Swimming Club' are split in the ratio
     males : females = 4 : 3

   (a) What fraction of the members are male?

   There are 140 members of the 'Dolphins Swimming Club'.

   (b) How many of these members are female?

6 A map is drawn to scale of
     1 : 500 000.
   The true distance between London and York is 331 kilometres.

> 1000 m = 1 km

   (a) Work out the distance, on the map, between London and York.
       Give your answer, in centimetres, correct to the nearest whole number.

   The distance on the map between Bristol and Cambridge is 53.4 cm.

   (b) Work out the true distance, in kilometres, between Bristol and Cambridge.
       Give your answer correct to the nearest kilometre.

7 Mr Smith wins £1200.
   He shares his winnings between himself, his wife and his son in the ratio
     4 : 3 : 1
   Calculate the amount his wife gets.

8 Malika's father won £128.
   He shared the £128 between his three children in the ratio 6 : 3 : 1.
   Malika was given the biggest share.

   (a) Work out how much Malika received.

   Malika saved $\frac{2}{3}$ of her share.

   (b) Work out how much Malika saved.   [E]

Test yourself	**What to review**

1 Mrs Owen receives a take home salary of £1400 per month. She splits this money in the ratio

      spend : save = 5 : 2

Work out how much she will save each month.

Unit 17, Example 6
Unit 17, Example 6

---

2 To make a pudding large enough for 4 people, Jenny needs
    120 grams of butter
    2 large eggs
Work out the amount of butter and the number of eggs Jenny will need to make a similar pudding large enough for 10 people.

Unit 17, Sections 17.3 and 17.4
Unit 17, Sections 17.3 and 17.4

---

3 The true height of a house is 12 metres.
On his scale drawing, an architect has used a distance of 30 cm for the height of the house.
On the same scale drawing the width of the house is 42.5 cm.
(a) Work out the true width of the house.

Unit 17, Section 17.5
Unit 17, Section 17.5

(b) Work out the scale the architect is using as a ratio.
    Give your answer in the form
       $1 : n$

Unit 17, Section 17.2
Unit 17, Section 17.2

Test yourself answers

1 £400   **2** 300 g of butter 5 large eggs   **3 (a)** 17 metres **(b)** 1 : 40

8 Basic algebra

In algebra letters are often used to represent numbers.

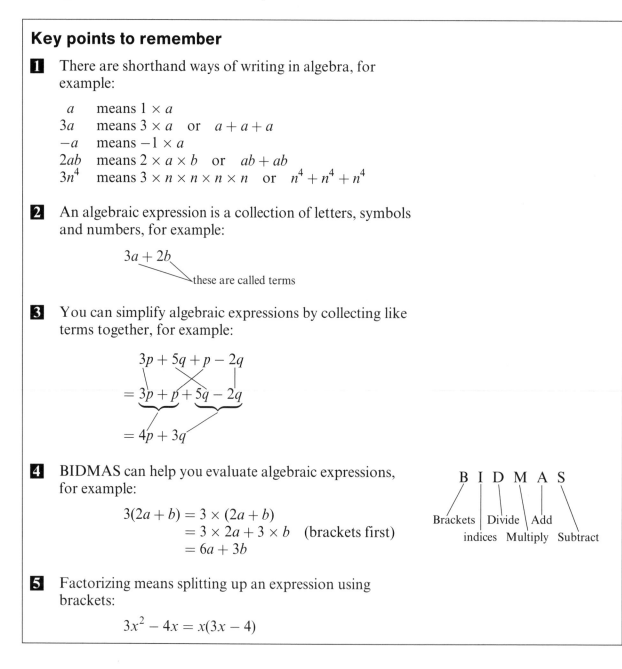

Key points to remember

1 There are shorthand ways of writing in algebra, for example:

a means $1 \times a$
$3a$ means $3 \times a$ or $a + a + a$
$-a$ means $-1 \times a$
$2ab$ means $2 \times a \times b$ or $ab + ab$
$3n^4$ means $3 \times n \times n \times n \times n$ or $n^4 + n^4 + n^4$

2 An algebraic expression is a collection of letters, symbols and numbers, for example:

$3a + 2b$

these are called terms

3 You can simplify algebraic expressions by collecting like terms together, for example:

$$3p + 5q + p - 2q$$
$$= 3p + p + 5q - 2q$$
$$= 4p + 3q$$

4 BIDMAS can help you evaluate algebraic expressions, for example:

$$3(2a + b) = 3 \times (2a + b)$$
$$= 3 \times 2a + 3 \times b \quad \text{(brackets first)}$$
$$= 6a + 3b$$

B I D M A S

Brackets | Divide \ Add
   indices Multiply Subtract

5 Factorizing means splitting up an expression using brackets:

$$3x^2 - 4x = x(3x - 4)$$

Example 1
(a) A cinema ticket costs £C.
   Write down an expression for the cost, in pounds of
     (i) 3 tickets   (ii) n tickets
(b) Expand the brackets and simplify
        $7(x + 2y) + 3(2x + y)$

(c) The diagram shows a cuboid.
The base is a square with sides of length x cm.
The height of the cuboid is h cm.
Find an expression for the volume, in cm^3, of the cuboid.

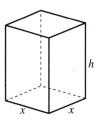

Answer

(a) (i) Using $\blacksquare$, the cost in pounds of 3 tickets is $3 \times C$, or $3C$.
(ii) Using $\blacksquare$, the cost in pounds of n tickets is $n \times C$, or nC.

(b) Using $\blacksquare$ and $\blacksquare$,

$$7(x + 2y) + 3(2x + y)$$
$$= 7 \times x + 7 \times 2y + 3 \times 2x + 3 \times y$$
$$= 7x + 14y + 6x + 3y$$
$$= 7x + 6x + 14y + 3y$$
$$= 13x + 17y$$

(c) Volume of a cuboid is given by
length of base $\times$ width of base $\times$ height

$$= x \times x \times h$$
$$= x^2 \times h$$
$$= x^2 h$$

Worked examination question [E]

In a football league a team gets 3 points for a win and 1 point for a draw.
(a) Team A won 6 games and drew 3 games.
How many points did they get?
(b) Team B won w games and drew d games.
Write down an expression for the number of points team b got.

Answer

(a) Team A got
$$3 \times 6 + 1 \times 3 = 18 + 3 = 21 \text{ points}$$

(b) Using $\blacksquare$ and $\blacksquare$, the expression is
$$3 \times w + 1 \times d$$
$$= 3w + d$$

Example 2

Factorize
(a) $4x + 12y$ (b) $4ab - 5ac$

Using $\blacksquare$
(a) $4x + 12y = 4(x + 3y)$
(b) $4ab - 5ac = a(4b - 5c)$

Revision exercise 8

1 The diagram shows a regular hexagon.

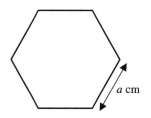

a cm

Perimeter = total distance around edge of shape

Each side of the hexagon has a length of a cm.
Write down an expression for the perimeter of the hexagon.

2 Write in symbols, the rule
'to find m, multiply n by 4 and then add 1'.

3 The diagram shows a rectangle.

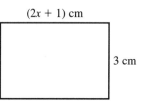

$(2x + 1)$ cm

3 cm

The width of the rectangle is 3 cm.
The length of the rectangle is $(2x + 1)$ cm.
Write down and simplify an expression for
(a) the perimeter, in cm, of the rectangle
(b) the area, in cm^2, of the rectangle.

Area of rectangle = length × width

4 A computer costs £C.
A printer costs £P.
Write down an expression for the total cost in pounds of
(a) a computer and a printer
(b) 2 computers and a printer.

5 Simplify
(a) $3a - 2b + 5a + 3b - 4a$
(b) $2(x + 3y) - x - 2y$.

6 Simplify
(a) $3(p + 2q) - 2(p + q)$
(b) $4(p + 3q) - 2(p - 5q)$.

7 Tickets for a concert cost £p.
Write down an expression for the total cost of
(a) 5 tickets for the concert
(b) n tickets for the concert.

8 The total cost of 5 equally priced CDs is £N.
Write down an expression for the cost of 1 CD.

9 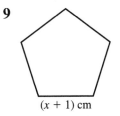 Write down an expression for the perimeter of this regular pentagon, in cm.
Each side has length $(x + 1)$ cm.

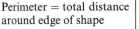
| Perimeter = total distance around edge of shape |

$(x + 1)$ cm

10 A coach has x passengers upstairs and y passengers downstairs.
    (a) Write down an expression, in terms of x and y, for the total number of passengers on the coach.

    Tickets for the journey cost £5 each.
    (b) Write down an expression, in terms of x and y, for the total amount of money paid by the passengers on the coach.   [E]

11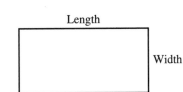

The width of the rectangle is x cm.
The length of the rectangle is 4 cm more than the width.
    (a) Write down an expression in terms of x for the length of the rectangle.

The perimeter of the rectangle is P cm.
    (b) Write down a formula for P in terms of x.   [E]

| Perimeter = total distance around edge of shape |

12 Factorize:
    (a) $3x + 6y$ **(b)** $a^2 + 4a$
    (c) $5a^2 - a$ **(d)** $7p^2 + p$

Test yourself	**What to review**
	If your answer is incorrect, review Foundation book:
1 Simplify $5x + 3y - 2y + x$	*Unit 2, Sections 2.3 and 2.4* Unit 2, Sections 2.3 and 2.4
2 Simplify $5p \times 3q$	*Unit 2, Sections 2.5 and 2.6* Unit 2, Sections 2.5 and 2.6
3 Expand and simplify $4(a + 2b) - 3(a - b)$	*Unit 2, Section 2.9* Unit 2, Section 2.9

| **Test yourself** | **What to review** |

If your answer is incorrect, review Foundation book:

4 The cost of a book is £b.
The cost of a pen is $3p$.
Georgie buys 5 of the books and 2 of the pens.
Write down an expression for the total cost of the books and pens bought by Georgie.

5 Factorise: $5 + 10a$

Unit 2, pages 40–41
Unit 2, pages 40–41

Test yourself answers

1 $6x + y$ **2** $15pq$ **3** $a + 11b$ **4** £$(5b + 2p)$ **5** $5(1 + 2a)$

9 Formulae

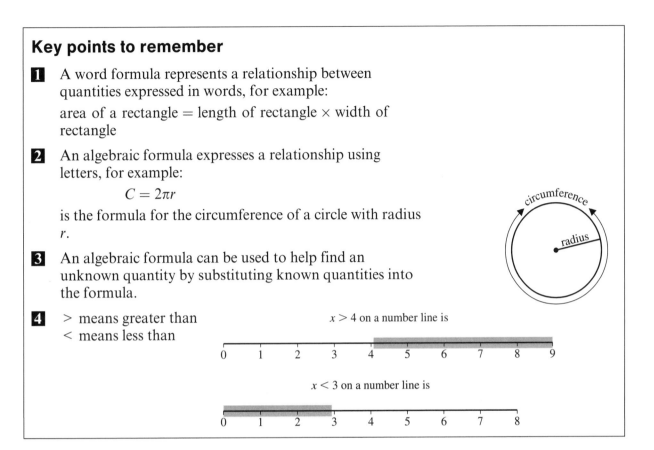

Key points to remember

1 A word formula represents a relationship between quantities expressed in words, for example:

area of a rectangle = length of rectangle × width of rectangle

2 An algebraic formula expresses a relationship using letters, for example:

$$C = 2\pi r$$

is the formula for the circumference of a circle with radius r.

3 An algebraic formula can be used to help find an unknown quantity by substituting known quantities into the formula.

4 > means greater than
< means less than

$x > 4$ on a number line is

$x < 3$ on a number line is

Example 1

The instructions for cooking a turkey are

'Allow 45 minutes per kilogram and then add on an extra 30 minutes'.

(a) Calculate the cooking time for a turkey weighing
    (i) 3 kg   (ii) 5.2 kg

The cooking time for a turkey weighing w kg is t minutes.

(b) Write down a formula connecting t and w.

Answer

(a) (i) Using **1**,

$$\text{time} = 3 \times 45 + 30$$
$$= 135 + 30 = 165 \text{ mins.}$$

(ii) Using **1**,

$$\text{time} = 5.2 \times 45 + 30$$
$$= 234 + 30 = 264 \text{ mins.}$$

(b) Using **2**,

$$\text{time} = 45 \times \text{weight} + 30$$

so $\quad t = 45 \times w + 30$

or $\quad t = 45w + 30$

Worked examination question [E]

$$p = \frac{2q + r}{6}$$

Find p when $q = 8.5$ and $r = 22$.

Answer

Using **3**,

$$p = \frac{2 \times 8.5 + 22}{6}$$

$$p = \frac{17 + 22}{6} = \frac{39}{6} = 6.5$$

Example 2

Draw a number line 0 to 10. Shade in the inequality $3 < \times 6$

Using **4**

Revision exercise 9

1 A formula used in science is

$$v = u + at$$

   (a) Calculate the value of v when
   (i) $u = 30, a = 10, t = 2$
   (ii) $u = 25, a = -3, t = 4$
   (iii) $u = 12, a = 2, t = 4.6$

   When $a = 3$ and $u = 24$ then $v = 36$.
   (b) Use this information to write down an equation for t.   [E]

2 In a football league a team gets 3 points for a win and 1 point for a draw.
   (a) Melchester United won 7 games and drew 5 games.
   How many points did they get?
   (b) Lucea Rovers got P points. They won x games and drew y games. Write down a formula connecting P, x and y.

3 Passengers on an aeroplane can carry at most 20 kilogrammes of luggage for each passenger.
   (a) An aeroplane has 150 passengers.
   What is the most luggage the aeroplane can carry?
   (b) An aeroplane has P passengers.
   The most luggage it can carry is l kilogrammes.
   Write down a formula connecting P and L.

4 The cost of hiring a van for a day is

'Twenty five pounds plus ten pence for every mile travelled'.

(a) Calculate the cost of hiring a van for a day and travelling 200 miles.

Mrs Robinson hires a van for a day.
She travels x miles in the van that day.
The total cost is £C.
(b) Write down a formula connecting C and x.

5 Write, in symbols, the rule

'To find y, multiply k buy 3 and then subtract 1'. [E]

6 The perimeter of this triangle is P cm.

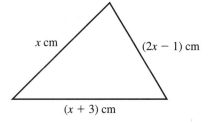

(a) Write down a formula for P in terms of x cm.
(b) Find the value of P when $x = 5$.

Perimeter = total distance around edge of shape

7 Here is a formula for working out the perimeter of a rectangle.

$P = 2(l + w)$

Use the formula to work out the value of P when $l = 6$ and $w = 4$. [E]

8

The diagram shows two pieces of wood placed end to end.
One piece is of length a, the other is of length $2b$.
The total length is L.
(a) Write a formula for L in terms of a and b.
(b) Use your formula to find L, when $a = 40$ cm and $b = 30$ cm.

9 Draw number lines from 0 to 10. Shade in these inequalities:
(a) $2 < x < 5$ **(b)** $5 < x < 7$
(c) $1 < x < 8$ **(d)** $3 > x > 0$

Test yourself	**What to review**

If your answer is incorrect,
review Foundation book:

1 Joanne works for a tele-sales company.
She earns

        £3 for each hour she works
        £16 for each sale she makes.

One evening Joanne worked for 4 hours and made 2 sales.

(a) Calculate how much Joanne earned that evening.

Unit 21, Section 21.1
Unit 21, Section 21.1

On another evening, Joanne earned £P.
She worked for h hours that evening and made s sales.

(b) Write down a formula connecting P, h and s.

Unit 21, Section 21.1
Unit 21, Section 21.1

---

2 $y = mx + c$

   (a) Calculate the value of y when

      (i) $x = 3$, $m = 5$ and $c = 7$
      (ii) $x = -2$, $m = -4$ and $c = 10$
      (iii) $x = 30$, $m = 1.8$ and $c = 32$
      (iv) $x = 12$, $m = 2\frac{1}{4}$ and $c = -3$

Unit 21, Sections 21.2 and 21.3
Unit 21, Sections 21.2 and 21.3

Test yourself answers

1   **(a)** £44   **(b)** $P = 3h + 16s$ **2 (a)** (i) 22   (ii) 18   (iii) 86   (iv) 24

10 Sequences: Number patterns

A pattern of numbers given in a definite order is called a sequence.

Key points to remember

1 Sequences can be represented by diagrams, for example:

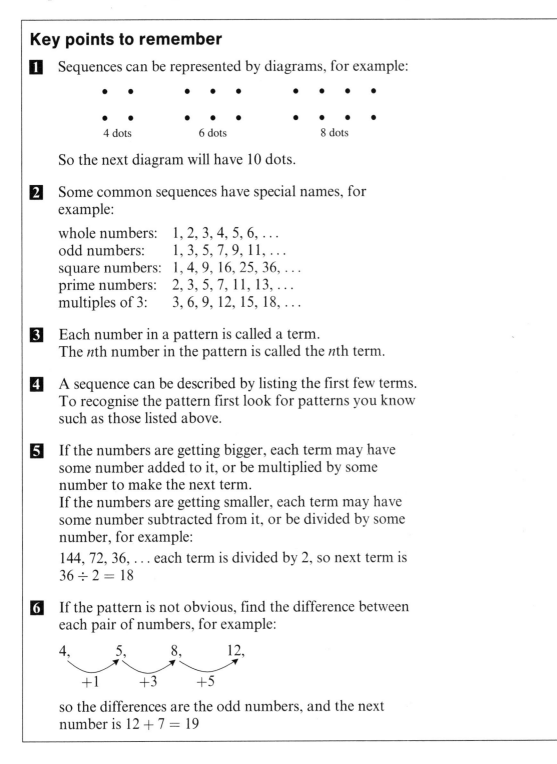

4 dots   6 dots   8 dots

So the next diagram will have 10 dots.

2 Some common sequences have special names, for example:

whole numbers: 1, 2, 3, 4, 5, 6, ...
odd numbers: 1, 3, 5, 7, 9, 11, ...
square numbers: 1, 4, 9, 16, 25, 36, ...
prime numbers: 2, 3, 5, 7, 11, 13, ...
multiples of 3:   3, 6, 9, 12, 15, 18, ...

3 Each number in a pattern is called a term.
The nth number in the pattern is called the nth term.

4 A sequence can be described by listing the first few terms.
To recognise the pattern first look for patterns you know such as those listed above.

5 If the numbers are getting bigger, each term may have some number added to it, or be multiplied by some number to make the next term.
If the numbers are getting smaller, each term may have some number subtracted from it, or be divided by some number, for example:

144, 72, 36, ... each term is divided by 2, so next term is $36 \div 2 = 18$

6 If the pattern is not obvious, find the difference between each pair of numbers, for example:

4,   5,   8,   12,
    +1   +3   +5

so the differences are the odd numbers, and the next number is $12 + 7 = 19$

> **7** To find the algebraic rule for a number pattern write the terms
> in a table with the term numbers and differences, for example:
>
> term number   1   2   3   4   5
> pattern   3,   8,   13,   18,   23, ...
>
> difference   +5   +5   +5   +5
>
> so the rule for any term is: add 3 each time.

Example 1

Julie makes a pattern out of matchsticks. The first four stages in
her pattern are shown below:

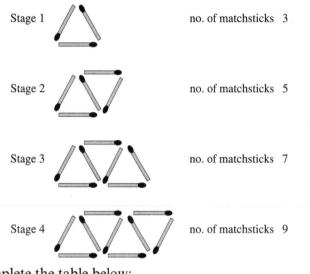

Stage 1   no. of matchsticks   3

Stage 2   no. of matchsticks   5

Stage 3   no. of matchsticks   7

Stage 4   no. of matchsticks   9

(a) Complete the table below:

Stage number	1	2	3	4	5	6
No. of matchsticks	3	5	7	9		

(b) Work out the number of matchsticks in stage 15 of Julie's
     pattern.
(c) Find, in words, a rule which will tell you how to work out the
     number of matchsticks in **any** stage of Julie's pattern.

Answer

(a) Using **1**, you could draw the next stages as

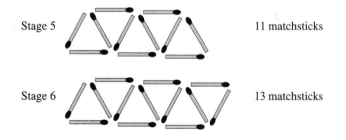

Stage 5   11 matchsticks

Stage 6   13 matchsticks

or, using **5** and **6** you could spot that the number pattern goes up like this:

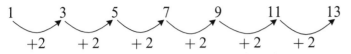

Either way the completed table is

Stage number	1	2	3	4	5	6
No. of matchsticks	3	5	7	9	11	13

(b) You could extend this table, by continually adding on 2 to get

Stage number	5	6	7	8	9	10	11	12	13	14	15
No. of matchsticks	11	13	15	17	19	21	23	25	27	29	31

but it is quicker if, using **7**, you can spot that

Stage number	No. of matchsticks
1	$3 = 2 \times 1 + 1$
2	$5 = 2 \times 2 + 1$
3	$7 = 2 \times 3 + 1$
4	$9 = 2 \times 4 + 1$
5	$11 = 2 \times 5 + 1$
6	$13 = 2 \times 6 + 1$

> Because the pattern goes up by 2 each time, we know that the formula is:
> $2 \times$ number $+$ something or
> $2 \times$ number $-$ something.

So, for stage 15,
number of matchsticks $= 2 \times 15 + 1 = 30 + 1$
$= 31$

(c) Using **7**, you should see that what is happening is:
add 2 each time

Worked examination question [E]

Here is a number pattern.
Two numbers are missing.

$$4, 8, 12, 16, \ldots, \ldots, 28,$$

(a) Find the two missing numbers.
(b) Describe in words, the rule that you used to find the missing numbers in the pattern.

Answer

(a) Using **5**,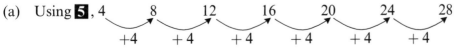

So the two missing numbers are 20 and 24.

(b)   One version of the rule is:

'add 4 to each number to find the next number'

or you could see that the first four numbers are the first four multiples of 4, so the rule is then:

'the numbers in the pattern are successive multiples of 4'

term number	pattern
1	$4 = 4 \times 1$
2	$8 = 4 \times 2$
3	$12 = 4 \times 3$
4	$16 = 4 \times 4$
$\vdots$	$\vdots$

Revision exercise 10

1 Here are the first five numbers in a simple sequence
$$80, 79, 77, 74, 70, \ldots, \ldots$$

(a) Find the next two numbers in the sequence.
(b) Work out the 10th number in the sequence.

2 Here is a number pattern.
Two numbers are missing.
$$6, 12, 18, \ldots, \ldots, 36.$$

(a) Copy the pattern and write in the missing numbers.
(b) Describe, in words, the rule that you used to find the missing numbers in the pattern.   [E]

3 Mr McDonald is making sheep pens. He uses fences to make pens as shown in the diagram below. The pens are arranged in a row.

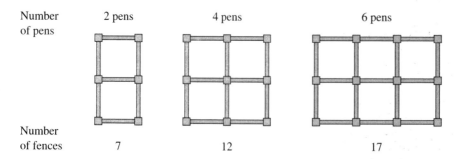

Number of pens   2 pens   4 pens   6 pens

Number of fences   7   12   17

(a) Draw diagrams to show the number of fences needed for
(i) 8 pens   (ii) 10 pens.
(b) Explain how you could work out the number of fences needed for twelve pens, without drawing a diagram.

The table below shows the number of fences needed for different numbers or pens.

Number of pens	2	4	6	8	10	12	14	16
Number of fences	7	12	17					

(c) Copy and complete the table.

(d) Work out the number of fences needed for 30 pens.   [E]

4 Here are the first five numbers in a simple number sequence.

   1, 3, 7, 13, 21, ..., ...

(a) Write down the next two numbers in the sequence.

(b) Describe, in words, the rule to continue this sequence.   [E]

5 Here are the first five numbers in a sequence.

   2, 5, 11, 23, 47, ...

The rule for working out the numbers in this sequence is

'You work out the next number by doubling the current number and then adding 1'

(a) Work out the 6th and 7th number in the sequence.

The 12th number in the sequence is 3071.

(b) work out the 11th number in the sequence.

6 (a) Write down the next two numbers in this number sequence.

   1, 7, 13, 19, 25, ..., ...

(b) Write down a number in the sequence that divides exactly by 5.   [E]

Test yourself

What to review

If your answer is incorrect, review Foundation book:

1 The diagram shows the dot pattern for the first three trapezium numbers.

1st	2nd	3rd
3 dots	7 dots	12 dots

(a) Complete the table below:

Trapezium number	1st	2nd	3rd	4th	5th
Number of dots	3	7	12		

Unit 2, pages 34–37
Unit 2, pages 45–47

Test yourself	What to review

(b) Work out the number of dots in the 10th trapezium number.   *Unit 2, pages 45–47*
Unit 2, pages 45–47

A certain trapezium number has 102 dots in its bottom row.
(c) (i) Which trapezium number will this be?   *Unit 2, pages 34–36*
      (ii) Explain how you worked out your answer.   Unit 2, pages 45–47
(d) Write down a rule for the number of dots in the next number   *Unit 2, pages 36–39*
      of the table.   Unit 2, pages 45–47

Test yourself answers

1 **(a)**

4th	5th
18	25

(b) 75

(c) (i) 100th
      (ii) The number of dots in the bottom row is always 2 more than the order of the trapezium number; or 100th trapezium number has 100 + 2 dots in its bottom row.
(d) Add one more than the last number added to get the current number, e.g. the first number is 3, so add 4, 5, 6, 7 . . . .

11 Simple equations

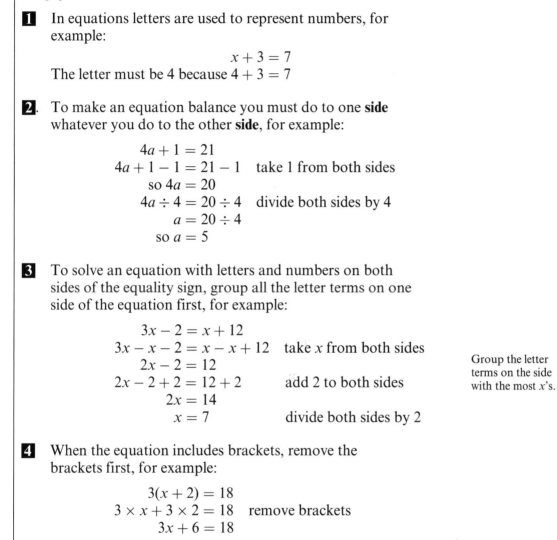

Key points to remember

1 In equations letters are used to represent numbers, for example:

$$x + 3 = 7$$

The letter must be 4 because $4 + 3 = 7$

2. To make an equation balance you must do to one **side** whatever you do to the other **side**, for example:

$$4a + 1 = 21$$
$$4a + 1 - 1 = 21 - 1 \quad \text{take 1 from both sides}$$
$$\text{so } 4a = 20$$
$$4a \div 4 = 20 \div 4 \quad \text{divide both sides by 4}$$
$$a = 20 \div 4$$
$$\text{so } a = 5$$

3 To solve an equation with letters and numbers on both sides of the equality sign, group all the letter terms on one side of the equation first, for example:

$$3x - 2 = x + 12$$
$$3x - x - 2 = x - x + 12 \quad \text{take } x \text{ from both sides}$$
$$2x - 2 = 12$$
$$2x - 2 + 2 = 12 + 2 \quad \text{add 2 to both sides}$$
$$2x = 14$$
$$x = 7 \quad \text{divide both sides by 2}$$

Group the letter terms on the side with the most x's.

4 When the equation includes brackets, remove the brackets first, for example:

$$3(x + 2) = 18$$
$$3 \times x + 3 \times 2 = 18 \quad \text{remove brackets}$$
$$3x + 6 = 18$$

Example 1

Solve the equation $\quad 4x + 7 = 29$

Answer

Using **2**,

$$4x + 7 - 7 = 29 - 7 \quad \text{subtract 7 from both sides}$$
$$4x = 22$$
$$4x \div 4 = 22 \div 4 \quad \text{divide both sides by 4}$$
$$x = 22 \div 4$$
$$x = 5.5$$

You can check your answer by substituting it into one side of the equation
L.H.S. $\quad 4 \times 5.5 + 7 = 22 + 7 = 29$
so the answer is correct.

Example 2

Solve the equation $5x - 3 = 3x + 17$

Answer

Using **2** and **3**,

$$5x - 3x - 3 = 3x + 17 - 3x \quad \text{subtract } 3x \text{ from both sides}$$
$$2x - 3 = 17$$

then

$$2x - 3 + 3 = 17 + 3 \quad \text{add 3 to both sides}$$
$$2x = 20$$
$$2x \div 2 = 20 \div 2 \quad \text{divide both sides by 2}$$
$$x = 20 \div 2$$
$$x = 10$$

Check:
LHS $5 \times 10 - 3 = 47$
RHS $3 \times 10 + 17 = 47$
LHS = RHS so answer is correct.

Example 3

Solve the equation $5(x - 3) = 20$

Answer

Using **4** and **2**,

$$5x - 15 = 20 \qquad \text{remove the brackets}$$
$$5x - 15 + 15 = 20 + 15 \quad \text{add 15 to both sides}$$
$$5x = 35$$
$$5x \div 5 = 35 \div 5 \qquad \text{divide both sides by 5}$$
$$x = 35 \div 5$$
$$x = 7$$

Remember to multiply each term in the bracket

Check:
LHS $5(7 - 3) = 5 \times 4 = 20$

Worked examination question [E]

Solve the following equations
(a) $4x + 2 = 27$
(b) $17 + 6y = 7 + y$

Answer

(a)   Using **2**,

$$4x + 2 = 27$$
$$4x + 2 - 2 = 27 - 2 \quad \text{subtract 2 from both sides}$$
$$4x = 25$$
$$4x \div 4 = 25 \div 4 \quad \text{divide both sides by 4}$$
$$x = 25 \div 4$$
$$x = 6\frac{1}{4}$$

Check:
LHS $4 \times 6\frac{1}{4} + 2 = 25 + 2 = 27.$

(b)   Using **2** and **3**,

$$17 + 6y = 7 + y$$
$$17 + 6y - y = 7 + y - y \quad \text{subtract } y \text{ from both sides}$$
$$17 + 5y = 7$$
$$17 - 17 + 5y = 7 - 17 \qquad \text{subtract 17 from both sides}$$
$$5y = -10$$

$$5y \div 5 = -10 \div 5 \qquad \text{divide both sides by 5}$$
$$y = -10 \div 5$$
$$y = -2$$

Check:
LHS $17 + 6 \times -2 = 17 - 12 = 5$
RHS $7 + -2 = 7 - 2 = 5$

Revision exercise 11

1 Solve the equations.
   (a) $4x - 7 = 20$ **(b)** $3(y + 5) = 42$ **(c)** $4x + 2 = 26$
   (d) $19 + 4y = 9 - y$ **(e)** $5x - 2 = 17$ **(f)** $4x - 3 = 3x + 7$
   (g) $3(x + 2) = 21$ **(h)** $2(x - 3) = x + 5$ **(i)** $4x + 3 = 17$
   (j) $5(x - 2) = 25$

2 Solve the equations.
   (a) $13 - 2y = 5$ **(b)** $7 - 2x = 11$ **(c)** $9 - 3x = 10$
   (d) $5 - 4x = 19$ **(e)** $7 + 2x = 1$ **(f)** $3x - 2 = 2x + 8$
   (g) $5 - 2x = 3 + x$ **(h)** $7 + 3x = 17 + x$ **(i)** $4 + 5x = 3x - 7$
   (j) $11x + 5 = x + 25$ **(k)** $\frac{1}{2}x - 3 = 2$ **(l)** $3k - 1 = 14$
   (m) $4p + 2 = -12$ **(n)** $5(x - 2) = 30$ **(o)** $4x - 2 = x + 8$

3 Solve the equations.
   (a) $2(y + 3) = 14$ **(b)** $3(2 - x) = 15$ **(c)** $4(y + 2) = 3y + 15$

4 Solve
   (a) $3x = 24$ **(b)** $18 + 3y = 6 - y$ [E]

Test yourself   What to review

<table>
<tr><td></td><td>If your answer is incorrect, review Foundation book:</td></tr>
<tr><td>1 Solve the equation $5x + 3 = 24$</td><td>Unit 15, Example 5
Unit 15, Example 5</td></tr>
<tr><td>2 Solve the equation $5p - 1 = 3p + 7$</td><td>Unit 15, Example 11
Unit 15, Example 11</td></tr>
<tr><td>3 Solve the equation $3(y - 2) = 2y + 8$</td><td>Unit 15, Example 12
Unit 15, Example 12</td></tr>
</table>

Test yourself answers
1 $x = 4.2$ (or $4\frac{1}{5}$)   **2** $p = 4$ **3** $y = 14$

12 Graphs 1: Straight lines

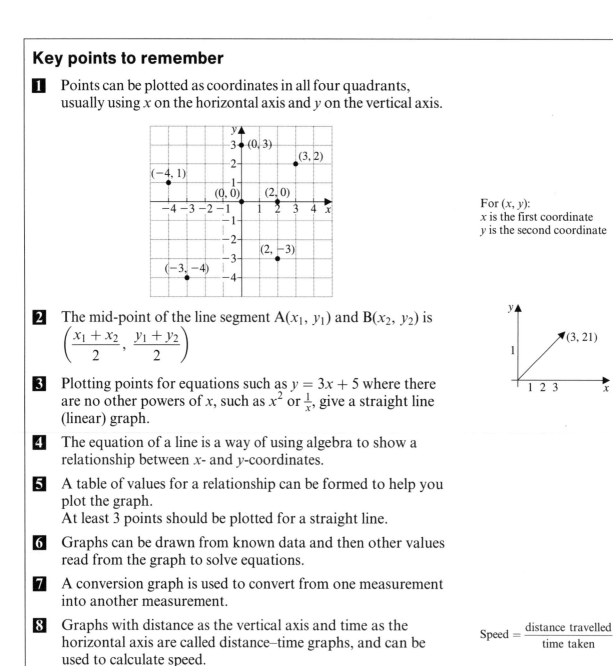

Key points to remember

1 Points can be plotted as coordinates in all four quadrants, usually using x on the horizontal axis and y on the vertical axis.

For (x, y):
x is the first coordinate
y is the second coordinate

2 The mid-point of the line segment A(x_1, y_1) and B(x_2, y_2) is
$$\left(\frac{x_1 + x_2}{2}, \frac{y_1 + y_2}{2}\right)$$

3 Plotting points for equations such as $y = 3x + 5$ where there are no other powers of x, such as x^2 or $\frac{1}{x}$, give a straight line (linear) graph.

4 The equation of a line is a way of using algebra to show a relationship between x- and y-coordinates.

5 A table of values for a relationship can be formed to help you plot the graph.
At least 3 points should be plotted for a straight line.

6 Graphs can be drawn from known data and then other values read from the graph to solve equations.

7 A conversion graph is used to convert from one measurement into another measurement.

8 Graphs with distance as the vertical axis and time as the horizontal axis are called distance–time graphs, and can be used to calculate speed.

$$\text{Speed} = \frac{\text{distance travelled}}{\text{time taken}}$$

Example 1
Work out the mid-point of the line segment AB where A is (1, 4) and B is (5, 9).
Using **2**,

$$x \text{ mid-point is } \frac{1+5}{2} = \frac{6}{2} = 3 \qquad y \text{ mid-point is } \frac{4+9}{2} = \frac{13}{2} = 6.5$$

So mid-point is (3, 6.5).

Example 2

The table shows the distance in miles a car can travel for various numbers of gallons of petrol.

gallons	1	2	3	4	5
miles	32	64	96	128	160

(a) Plot this information on a graph.
(b) Use your graph to work out
   (i) the distance the car will travel on 3.5 gallons of petrol
   (ii) the number of gallons needed for the car to travel 88 miles
   (iii) the distance the car can travel on 7 gallons of petrol.

Answer

(a) Using **5** and **6**,
the graph is a straight line.

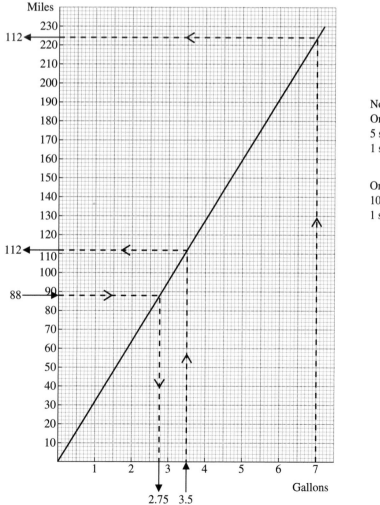

Note:
On the vertical axis,
5 squares = 10 miles so
1 square = 2 miles.

On the horizontal axis,
10 squares 5 1 gallon
1 square = 1 ÷ 10
       = 0.1 gallons.

(b) (i)   Using **6**,
          when the number of gallons = 3.5
          then the distance = 112 miles.
    (ii) Using **6**,
          when the distance = 88 miles
          then the number of gallons = 2.75.
    (iii) You need to extend the straight line to 7 gallons
          Using **6** when the number of gallons = 7
          then the distance = 224 miles.

Worked examination question 1 [E]

The graph shows the distance travelled by a van in the first 30 seconds after it passed a road junction.

(a) Use the graph to find the distance travelled by the van in the first 15 seconds after it passed the road junction.

(b) Calculate the speed of the van over the first 15 seconds after it passed the road junction.

(c) Describe fully the journey of the van during the first 30 seconds after it passed the road junction.

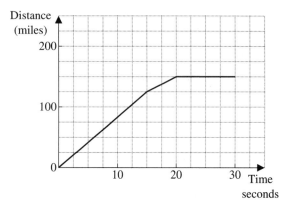

Answer

(a) Using **8**,
    over the first 15 seconds, the journey of the van is represented by

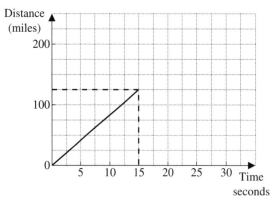

Note:
On the vertical axis,
4 squares = 100 miles so
1 square = 100 ÷ 4
        = 25 miles

So in 15 seconds it travelled 125 metres.

(b) Using **8** and **6**,
    the speed of the van is

$$\frac{\text{distance}}{\text{time}} = \frac{125}{15} = 8.33 \text{ metres/second (to 2 d.p.)}$$

(c) Using **8** and **6**,
    it is best to label the journey in 3 sections.

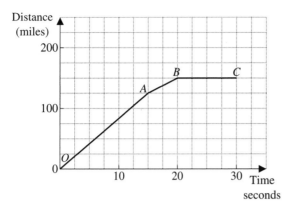

For section OA, the first 15 seconds, the van travels 125 m at a speed of 8.33 metres/second.

For section AB, the next 5 seconds, the van travels a further 25 metres.

This will be at a speed of $\frac{25}{5} = 5$ metres/second.

For section BC, the final 10 seconds, the van does not travel any further distance. So it is stopped for these 10 seconds.

Worked examination question 2 [E]

(a) Complete the table of values for $y = 3x - 2$.

x	-1	0	1	2	3
$y = 3x - 2$					

(b) On a grid plot your values for x and y. Join your points with a straight line.

(c) Write down the coordinates of the point where your graph crosses the y-axis.

Answer

(a) Using **5**,

x	y
-1	$3(-1) - 2 = -3 - 2 = -5$
0	$3(0) - 2 = 0 - 2 = -2$
1	$3(1) - 2 = 3 - 2 = 1$
2	$3(2) - 2 = 6 - 2 = 4$
3	$3(3) - 2 = 9 - 2 = 7$

so table is:

x	-1	0	1	2	3
$y = 3x - 2$	-5	-2	1	4	7

(b)   Using **1** and **3**, the graph is

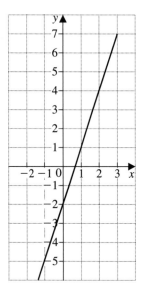

(c)   Using **6**,
      the graph crosses the y-axis at the point with coordinates
      $(0, -2)$.

Worked examination question 3 [E]

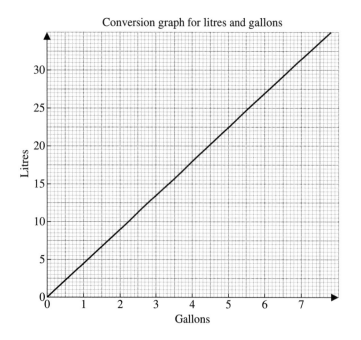

Conversion graph for litres and gallons

Use the conversion graph to convert
(a)   4 gallons into litres
(b)   27 litres into gallons.

Answer

(a) Using **7**, go up from 4 gallons to the line and across to 18 litres.

(b) Using **7**,
go across from 27 litres to the line and down to 6 gallons.

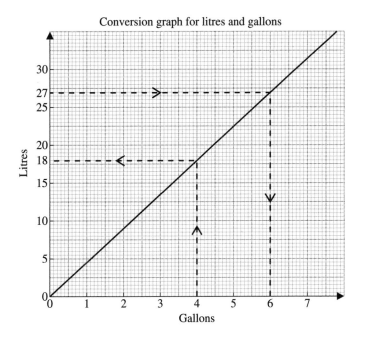

On the verical axis
10 squares = 5 litres so
1 square = 5 ÷ 10 = 0.5 litres

Revision exercise 12

1 (a) Write down the coordinates of the points
   (i) P   (ii) R

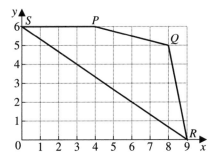

(b) Copy the coordinate grid above and plot the following points

   T(1, 2),   V(4, 1).   [E]

(c) Work out the mid-point of the line segment SR.

2 This is a conversion graph for miles and kilometres.

(a) How many miles are equivalent to 32 kilometres?

(c) How many kilometres are equivalent to 15 miles?

[E]

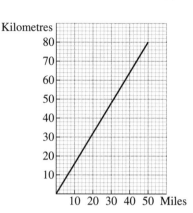

3 The graph represents $y = 3x - 2$.

(a) When $x = 2$, find the value of y.

(b) When $y = -5$, find the value of x.

(c) Explain whether or not the line $y = 3x - 2$ passes through the point (10, 27).   [E]

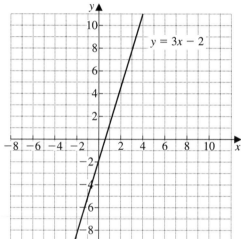

4 Errol's house has a meter which measures the amount of water he uses.

Errol can pay on Tariff A for the number of water units that he uses.

The graph can be used to find out how much he must pay for his water on Tariff A.

(a) Use the graph to find how much he must pay when he uses

(i) 60 units   (ii) 104 units.

Instead of Tariff A, Errol could pay for his water on Tariff B.

The table shows how much Errol would have to pay for his water on Tariff B.

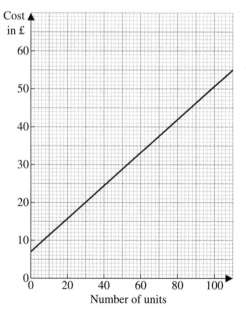

Number of water units used	0	20	40	60	80	100
Cost in £	12	18	24	30	36	42

(b) Plot a graph on a copy of the grid to show this information.   [E]

5 Jim cycles from his home to a shop.
He does the shopping then he cycles back home.

This information is represented on the distance–time graph below.

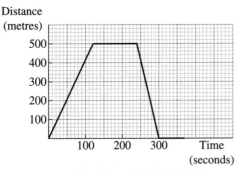

(a) How far is it from Jim's home to the shop?
(b) How long did Jim spend doing the shopping
   (i) in seconds
   (ii) in minutes?
(c) Calculate Jim's speed, in metres per second
   (i) in cycling from his home to the shop
   (ii) in cycling from the shop back to his home.

6 (a) Complete the table of values for
$$y = 4x + 1$$

x	−2	−1	0	1	2	3
y		−3				

(b) Draw the graph of
$$y = 4x + 1$$
for values of x from −2 to 3.
(c) On the same axes draw the graph of
$$y = 2x.$$
(d) Write down the coordinates of the point where the two graphs cross.

7 (a) Copy and complete the table for $y = 2x - 9$

x	y
0	
5	
10	

(b) Draw the graph of $y = 2x - 9$.
Your grid should go from 0 to 15 on the x-axis and from −10 to 15 on the y-axis.
(c) Find the point on the line $y = 2x - 9$ for which $y = x$.
State the coordinates of this point.   [E]

8 (a) Copy and complete this table of values for $y = 3x - 1$

x	-2	-1	0	1	2	3
y			-1			

(b) Draw the graph of $y = 3x - 1$.
Your grid should go from -5 to 5 on the x-axis and from -8 to 8 on the y-axis.

(c) Use your graph to find
  (i)   the value of x when $y = 3.5$
  (ii) the value of y when $x = -1.5$.

Test yourself	**What to review**

If your answer is incorrect, review Foundation book:

1 Emma turns on a tap.
The table shows the volume of water, in cubic centimetres, coming out of the tap in the first 6 seconds.

Time (seconds)	1	2	3	4	5	6
Volume (cc)	35	70	105	140	175	210

(a) Plot this information on a graph.

Unit 9, Examples 1 and 2
Unit 9, Examples 2 and 3

(b) Use your graph to find the volume of water coming out of the tap in 3.6 secs.

Unit 9, Examples 1 and 2
Unit 9, Examples 2 and 3

(c) Use your graph to find the time it takes for 182 cc of water to come out of the tap.

Unit 9, Examples 1 and 2
Unit 9, Examples 2 and 3

Emma fills a vase out of the tap.
The capacity of the vase is litre.

(d) Work out how long it will take Emma to fill the vase if
1 litre = 1000 cc
Give your answer, in seconds, to one decimal place.

Unit 9, Examples 1 and 2
Unit 9, Examples 2 and 3

2 (a) Complete the table of values for $y = 3x - 5$.

Unit 9, Section 9.5
Unit 9, Section 9.5

x	-2	-1	0	1	2	3
y						

(b) Draw the graph of $y = 3x - 5$.

Unit 9, Section 9.5
Unit 9, Section 9.5

(c) Use your graph to work out
  (i)   the value of y when $x = 1\frac{1}{2}$
  (ii) the value of x when $y = 1\frac{1}{2}$.

Unit 9, Section 9.5
Unit 9, Section 9.5

Test yourself

If your answer is incorrect,
review Foundation book:

Unit 9, Section 9.3
Unit 9, Section 9.3

3 The diagram shows a
conversion graph
which converts degrees
Celsius (°C) to degrees
Fahrenheit (°F).
Use your graph
  (a) to convert 60°C
       to °F.
  (b) to convert 113°F
       to °C.

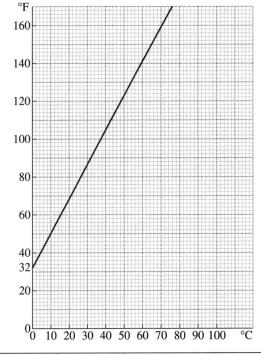

Test yourself answers

1 (a) Vol (cc)

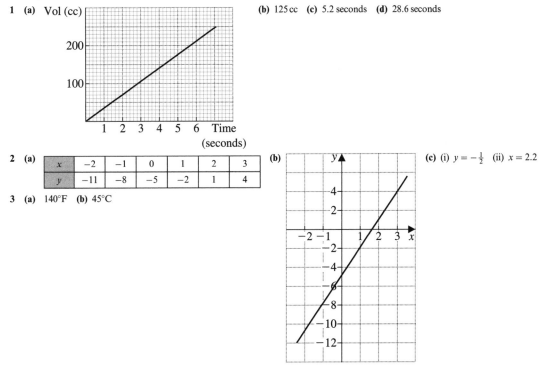

(b) 125 cc   **(c)** 5.2 seconds   **(d)** 28.6 seconds

2 (a)

x	−2	−1	0	1	2	3
y	−11	−8	−5	−2	1	4

(b)

(c) (i) $y = -\frac{1}{2}$ (ii) $x = 2.2$

3 (a) 140°F   **(b)** 45°C

13 Graphs 2: Curves

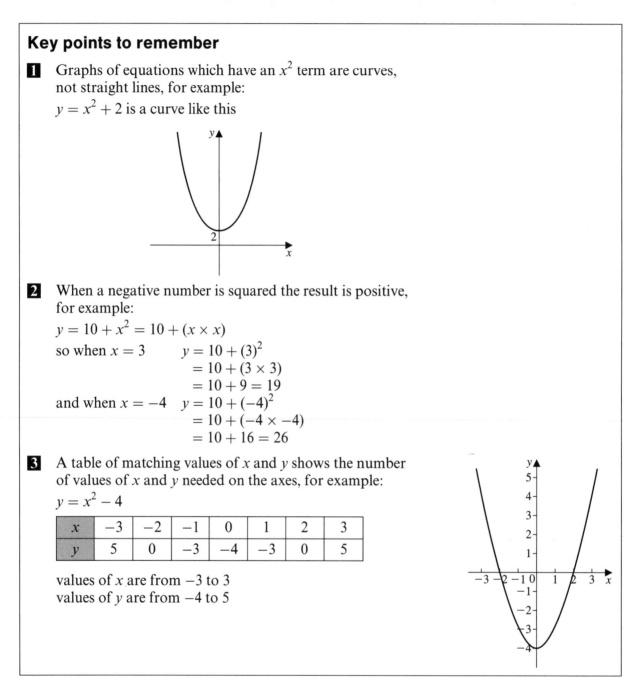

Key points to remember

1 Graphs of equations which have an x^2 term are curves, not straight lines, for example:

$y = x^2 + 2$ is a curve like this

2 When a negative number is squared the result is positive, for example:

$y = 10 + x^2 = 10 + (x \times x)$

so when $x = 3$ $y = 10 + (3)^2$
$= 10 + (3 \times 3)$
$= 10 + 9 = 19$

and when $x = -4$ $y = 10 + (-4)^2$
$= 10 + (-4 \times -4)$
$= 10 + 16 = 26$

3 A table of matching values of x and y shows the number of values of x and y needed on the axes, for example:

$y = x^2 - 4$

x	-3	-2	-1	0	1	2	3
y	5	0	-3	-4	-3	0	5

values of x are from -3 to 3
values of y are from -4 to 5

Example 1

(a) Complete the table of values for the equation

$$y = x^2 + 5$$

x	-3	-2	-1	0	1	2	3
$y = x^2 + 5$		9					

(b) Draw the graph of

$$y = x^2 + 5$$

for the values of x from -3 to 3.

Answer

(a) Using **3**, where

$$
\begin{array}{llll}
x = 3 & y = x^2 + 5 & y = 3^2 + 5 = 3 \times 3 + 5 = 9 + 5 = 14 \\
x = 2 & y = x^2 + 5 & y = 2^2 + 5 = 2 \times 2 + 5 = 4 + 5 = \;\;9 \\
x = 1 & y = x^2 + 5 & y = 1^2 + 5 = 1 \times 1 + 5 = 1 + 5 = \;\;6 \\
x = 0 & y = x^2 + 5 & y = 0^2 + 5 = 0 \times 0 + 5 = 0 + 5 = \;\;5 \\
x = -1 & y = x^2 + 5 & y = (-1)^2 + 5 = -1 \times -1 + 5 = 1 + 5 = \;\;6 \\
x = -2 & y = x^2 + 5 & y = (-2)^2 + 5 = -2 \times -2 + 5 = 4 + 5 = \;\;9 \\
x = -3 & y = x^2 + 5 & y = (-3)^2 + 5 = -3 \times -3 + 5 = 9 + 5 = 14
\end{array}
$$

So the completed table is

x	-3	-2	-1	0	1	2	3
$y = x^2 + 5$	14	9	6	5	6	9	14

(b) Using **1**,
the graph of $y = x^2 + 5$ is shown on the right.

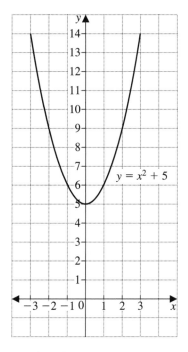

(Note: It helps to recognise that

- the graph is a smooth curve – with no kinks or flat parts.
- the curve is symmetrical about the y-axis (or the vertical axis).
- the curve $y = x^2 + 5$ passes through the point $(0, 5)$; so when $x = 0, y = 5$.)

Revision exercise 13

1 (a) Complete the table of values for the equation

$$y = x^2 - 5$$

x	−4	−3	−2	−1	0	1	2	3	4
y				−4					

(b) Draw the graph of $y = x^2 - 5$ for values of x from −4 to 4.

2 For values of x from −5 to 5, draw the graphs of
(a) $y = x^2$ **(b)** $y = 2x^2$

3 (a) Draw the graph of

$$y = x^2$$

for values of x from −4 to 4.
(b) On the same axes draw the graph of

$$y = 3x$$

(c) State the coordinates of the two points where the graphs cross.

4 (a) Use the equation $y = x + 3$ to complete the table of values:

x	−3	−2	−1	0	1	2	3
y	0			3		5	

(b) Use the equation $y = x^2$ to complete the table of values:

x	−3	−2	−1	0	1	2	3
y						4	

(c) Draw the graphs of

$$y = x + 3 \text{ and } y = x^2$$

on the same grid.   [E]

Test yourself   **What to review**

If your answer is incorrect,
review Foundation book:

1 (a) Complete the table of values for the equation $y = x^2 + 3$ *Unit 9, pages 131*
Unit 9, page 155

x	-4	-3	-2	-1	0	1	2	3	4
y									

(b) Draw the graph of the equation $y = x^2 + 3$ for values of x *Unit 9, page 131*
from -4 to 4.   Unit 9, page 155

(c) On the same axes, draw the graph of $y = 10 - x$ for values of   *Unit 9, pages 126–129*
x from -4 to 4.   Unit 9, pages 151–154

(d) Write down the coordinates of the two points where the   *Unit 9, Worked exam question 1*
graphs cross.   Unit 9, Worked exam question 1

Test yourself answers

1 (a)

x	-4	-3	-2	-1	0	1	2	3	4
y	19	12	7	4	3	4	7	12	19

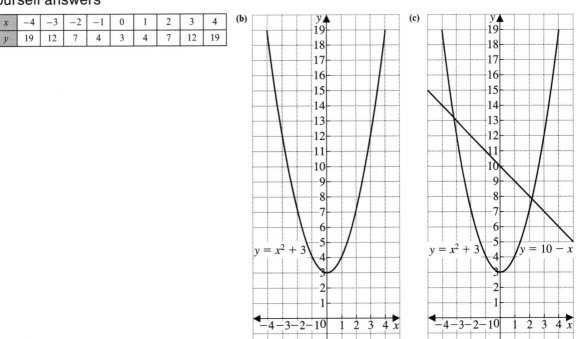

(d) (2.2, 7.8) (−3.2, 13.2)

14 Measure

Key points to remember

1 Lengths and distances are measured in metric and imperial units.

metric: 10 mm = 1 cm   imperial: 12 inches = 1 foot
         100 cm = 1 m   3 feet = 1 yard
        1000 mm = 1 m   1760 yards = 1 mile
         1000 m = 1 km

2 Capacity is the measure of the amount a container can hold. It is measured in:

metric: 100 cl   = 1 litre   imperial: 8 pints = 1 gallon
        1000 ml   = 1 litre
        1000 litre = 1 cubic metre = 1 m^3

3 Weight (mass) is measured in these units:

metric: 1000 mg = 1 g   imperial: 16 ounces = 1 pound
        1000 g   = 1 kg   14 pounds = 1 stone
        1000 kg = 1 tonne   8 stone = 1 hundredweight
                           20 hundredweight = 1 ton

4 The approximate metric and imperial conversions are:

Metric	Imperial
8 km	5 miles
1 kg	2.2 pounds
25 g	1 ounce
1 *l*	1.75 pints
4.5 *l*	1 gallon
1 m	39 inches
2.5 cm	1 inch
30 cm	1 foot

These conversions are not always given in an exam. You need to know them.

5 Time can be given as 12-hour clock times or 24-hour clock times.

12 hour	24-hour
8:25 am	08:25
4:50 pm	16:50
9 pm	21:00

6 The measures of time are:

60 seconds = 1 minute   365 days = 1 year
60 minutes = 1 hour   366 days = 1 leap year
24 hours = 1 day   12 months = 1 year

Example 1
The distance from London to Manchester is approximately 195 miles.
Work out the approximate distance in km from London to Manchester.

Answer
Using **4**,
$$5 \text{ miles} = 8 \text{ km}$$
$$1 \text{ mile} = \tfrac{8}{5} \text{ km}$$
$$\text{Then } 195 \text{ miles} = \tfrac{8}{5} \times 195$$
$$= 312 \text{ km}$$

There is more on the unitary method in Unit 7.

Worked examination question 1 [E]
A train left London at 08:55 and arrived at Manchester at 12:02.
How many minutes did the journey take?

Answer
Using **5**,   time taken = 3 hours 7 minutes
Using **6**,   3 hours = 3 × 60 minutes
$$= 180 \text{ minutes}$$
Total minutes for whole journey = 180 + 7
$$= 187 \text{ minutes}$$

+1 hr (0855
+1 hr (0955
+1 hr (1055
+7 min (1155
       (1202

Worked examination question 2 [E]
A bag of flour weighs 1.5 kilograms.
(a)   Change 1.5 kilograms to grams.
(b)   Change 1.5 kilograms to pounds.

Answer
(a)   Using **3**,   1.5 kilograms = 1.5 × 1000 grams
$$= 1500 \text{ grams}$$
(b)   Using **4**,   1 kg = 2.2 pounds
$$1.5 \text{ kg} = 1.5 \times 2.2 \text{ pounds}$$
$$= 3.3 \text{ pounds}$$

Remember: 'kilo' means a thousand

Revision exercise 14

1 Jackie measures her height. How tall is she?

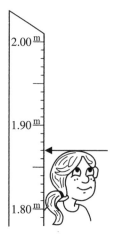

2 The picture shows the scale on the side of a kettle.

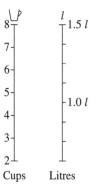

How many litres of water are needed to fill 5 cups?

3 Write down the readings shown on these scales.

(a)

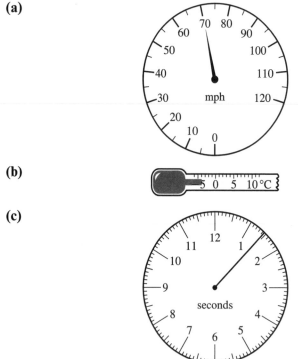

(b)

(c)

4 The diagram shows some potatoes on a set of scales.
(a) Write down the weight of the potatoes.

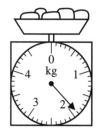

Fred buys some apples.
They weigh 3.65 kilograms.
(b) Copy the diagram and draw a pointer showing 3.65 kilograms on the scale.
(c) Work out the approximate weight of the apples in pounds.

In part **(d)** you must write down the units in the answer.
The cost of apples is 99p per kilogram.
(d) Work out the total cost of 3.65 kg of apples. [E]

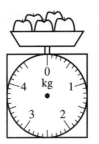

5 **(a)** One afternoon James' watch looked like this.
Write down the same time as it would appear on a digital display.
(b) Jim's digital watch shows the time.

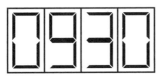

Draw the hands on a watch face to show the same time as the digital watch. [E]

6 Keith went to the cinema. When he arrived, the reading on his digital watch was 15:30.
(a) Write 15:30 using pm.

The times at which the films start and how long they last are shown on the right. Keith decided to see The Pelican Brief.
(b) (i) Write down the earliest time that he could see this film.
(ii) How long, in minutes, did he have to wait before it started?
(iii) At the end of the film, what was the reading on his digital watch? [L]

SCREEN CINEMA
ITS AN EXPERIENCE TO REMEMBER
PERFORMANCE TIMES FOR FRIDAY, 4TH MARCH TO THURSDAY, 10TH MARCH ONLY

PHILADELPHIA (12)
2 hrs 19 mins
All days 1.00 3.40 6.40 9.30
Fri & Sat Late Shows 12.15

THE PELICAN BRIEF (12)
2 hrs 35 mins
All days 12.30 3.45 6.50 9.45

MRS DOUBTFIRE (12)
2 hrs 20 mins
All days 12.45 3.30 6.30 9.20
Fri & Sat Late Shows 12.05

FREE WILLY (U)
2 hrs 5 mins
All days 1.30 3.55 6.20
Sat Early Show 11.00

SCHINDLERS LIST (15)
3 hrs 28 mins
Fri & Sat 2.10 6.10 10.10
Sun-Thurs 12.00 4.00 8.00

THE REMAINS OF THE DAY (U)
2 hrs 29 mins
All days 4.15 7.10 10.00
Fri, Mon-Thurs Early Show 1.15

COOL RUNNINGS (PG)
1 hrs 54 mins
All days 2.05 4.30 6.55 9.15
Sat Early Show 11.30
Fri & Sat Late Shows 11.45

7 The distance from Clifton to Leeds is 187 miles. Work out the distance in kilometres, to the nearest kilometre.

8 A bus leaves the bus station at 16:34. It arrives at Manor Close 1 hour 37 minutes later.
At what time did the bus arrive at Manor Close?
Give your answer in 12-hour clock time and 24-hour clock time.

9 Estimate the height of an eight storey building.

Test yourself	What to review

If your answer is incorrect, review Foundation book:

1 Write 7:25 pm in 24-hour clock time.

Unit 7, pages 99–100
Unit 7, pages 117–118

2 Convert 256 km into miles.

Unit 13, Example 3
Unit 13, Example 3

3 Estimate the height of a double decker bus.

Unit 7, Section 7.2
Unit 7, Section 7.2

4 A train leaves Bristol at 08:13 and arrives at Paddington at 10:59.
   (a) How long has the train taken in minutes?

   (b) How long has it taken in hours and minutes.

Unit 13, Example 5(b)
Unit 13, Example 5(b)
Unit 13, Section 13.3
Unit 13, Section 13.3

Test yourself answers

1 19:25   2 160 miles   3 5–7 m   4 (a) 166 minutes (b) 2 hours 46 minutes

15 2-D shapes

Key points to remember

1 A triangle is a three-sided shape.
Some special triangles are:

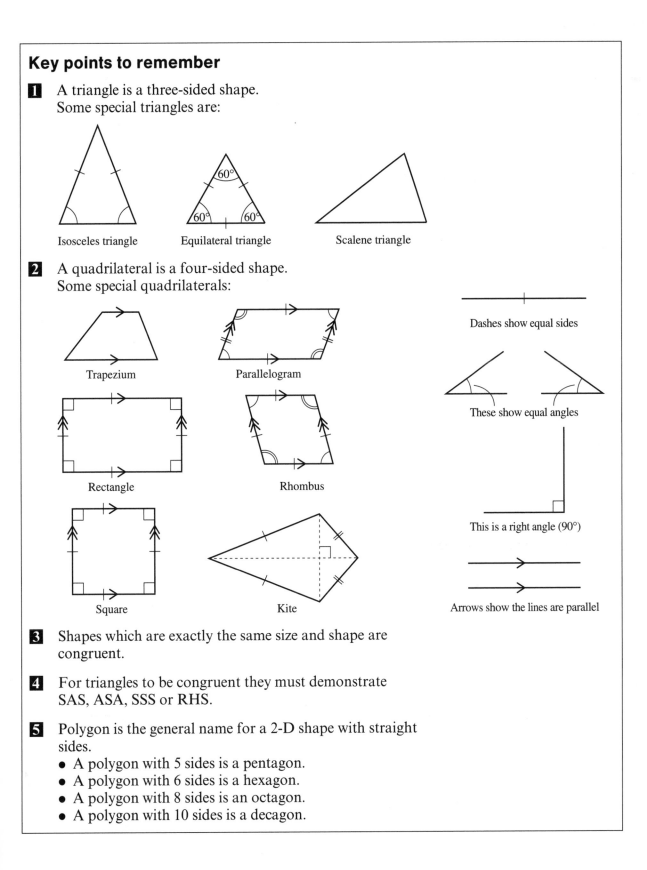

Isosceles triangle   Equilateral triangle   Scalene triangle

2 A quadrilateral is a four-sided shape.
Some special quadrilaterals:

Trapezium   Parallelogram

Dashes show equal sides

Rectangle   Rhombus

These show equal angles

This is a right angle (90°)

Square   Kite

Arrows show the lines are parallel

3 Shapes which are exactly the same size and shape are congruent.

4 For triangles to be congruent they must demonstrate SAS, ASA, SSS or RHS.

5 Polygon is the general name for a 2-D shape with straight sides.
- A polygon with 5 sides is a pentagon.
- A polygon with 6 sides is a hexagon.
- A polygon with 8 sides is an octagon.
- A polygon with 10 sides is a decagon.

6 A polygon is a regular polygon if all its sides are the same length and all the angles the same size.

7 For a polygon: interior angle + exterior angle = 180°.

8 The exterior angles of a polygon always add up to 360°. For a regular polygon with n sides, each exterior angle is 360 ÷ n.

9 A pattern of shapes which fit together without leaving any gaps or overlapping is called a tessellation.

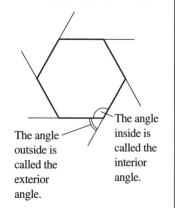

The angle outside is called the exterior angle.

The angle inside is called the interior angle.

Example 1

For this pair of triangles:
(i)   state if they are congruent;
(ii) give reasons to support your statement.

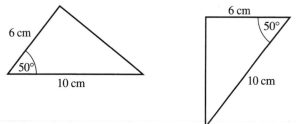

6 cm

6 cm

50°

10 cm

50°

10 cm

Using **3**
(i)   congruent

Using **4**
(ii) SAS

Worked examination question [E]

ABCDEF is a regular hexagon with centre O.
(Diagram not accurately drawn.)
(a)   What type of triangle is *ABO*?
(b)   (i)   Work out the size of the angle marked $x°$.
      (ii) Work out the size of the angle marked $y°$.
(c)   (i)   What type of quadrilateral is *BCDO*?
      (ii) Copy and draw lines on the diagram to show how three such quadrilaterals can tessellate to make a hexagon.
      (iii) What special mathematical word can be used to describe these three shapes?

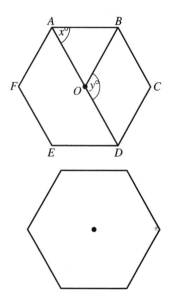

Answer

(a) Using **1**, ABO is an equilateral triangle.

(b) (i) As triangle ABO is equilateral, $x = 60°$.
     (ii) The quadrilateral $OBCD$ is the same as two equilateral triangles.
           So angle $BOD = 2 \times 60° = 120°$
           So $y = 120°$.

(c) (i) Using **2**, all sides of $BCDO$ are equal in length and opposite sides are parallel, so $BCDO$ is a rhombus.
     (ii) Using **9**

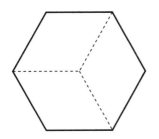

     (iii) Using **3**, they are congruent.

Revision exercise 15

1 **(a)** Write down the geometrical name of the quadrilateral drawn in the diagram.

Quadrilaterals identical to the one in **(a)** are to be used to tessellate the inside of a rectangle.

(b) Show how the tessellation can be drawn on a grid.   [E]

2 Sketches of a rectangle, parallelogram and trapezium are shown below. Equal sides, parallel sides and equal angles are marked.

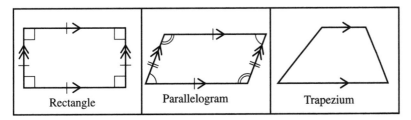

(a) Sketch a square, a rhombus and a kite. Mark equal sides, parallel sides and equal angles.

(b) Which of the quadrilaterals have four equal angles?

(c) A rhombus is a special type of parallelogram as it possesses **all** the properties of a parallelogram.
Which other special types of quadrilateral can a rhombus be?

[E]

3 Write down the letters of the shapes that are congruent.

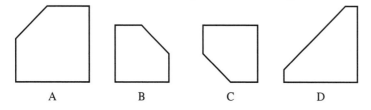

4 Work out
  (a) the size of the exterior angles of a decagon
  (b) the size of the interior angles of a decagon.

5 Draw accurately a rectangle that measures 3.1 cm by 2.4 cm.

6 (a) Name this shape.

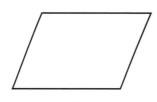

  (b) Show how this shape can tessellate.

7 The diagram on the right shows five congruent isosceles triangles.
A base angle is 70°.
Calculate the size of the angle marked x.   [E]

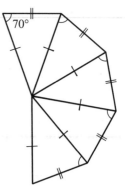

8

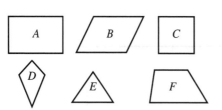

Explain how shape E is different from the other shapes.   [E]

9 For each pair of triangles:
  (i) say if they are congruent;
  (ii) if they are congruent give a reason.

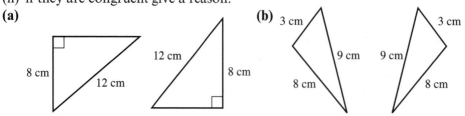

Test yourself	What to review

If your answer is incorrect,
review Foundation book:

1 Name this shape.

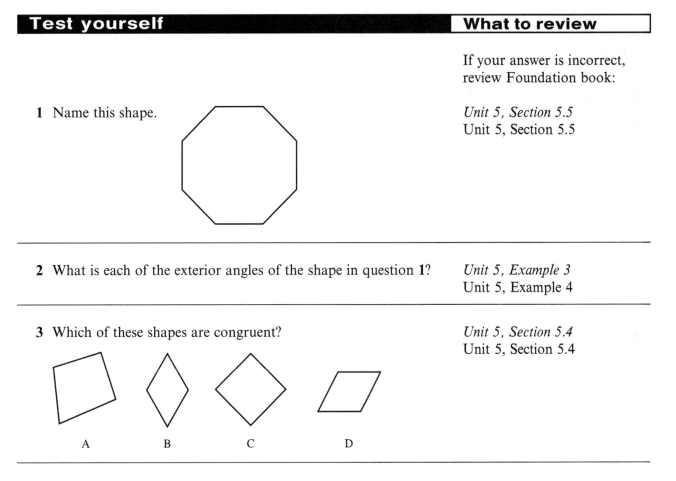

Unit 5, Section 5.5
Unit 5, Section 5.5

2 What is each of the exterior angles of the shape in question **1**?

Unit 5, Example 3
Unit 5, Example 4

3 Which of these shapes are congruent?

A   B   C   D

Unit 5, Section 5.4
Unit 5, Section 5.4

Test yourself answers

1 regular octagon   **2** 45°   **3** B and D

16 Angles

An angle is a measure of turn.

Key points to remember

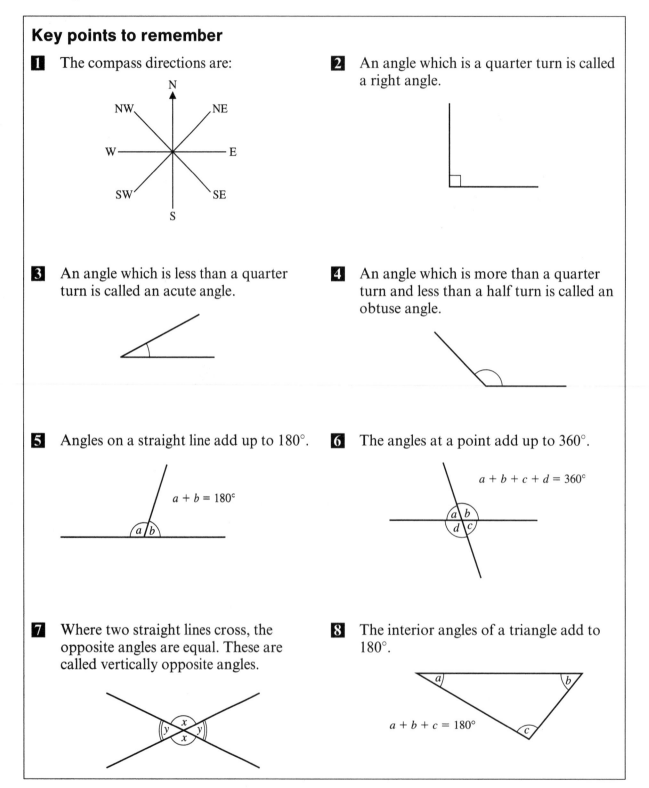

1 The compass directions are:

2 An angle which is a quarter turn is called a right angle.

3 An angle which is less than a quarter turn is called an acute angle.

4 An angle which is more than a quarter turn and less than a half turn is called an obtuse angle.

5 Angles on a straight line add up to 180°.

$a + b = 180°$

6 The angles at a point add up to 360°.

$a + b + c + d = 360°$

7 Where two straight lines cross, the opposite angles are equal. These are called vertically opposite angles.

8 The interior angles of a triangle add to 180°.

$a + b + c = 180°$

9 The interior angles of a quadrilateral add up to 360°.

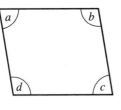

$$a + b + c + d = 360°$$

10 Lines which remain the same distance apart are called parallel lines.

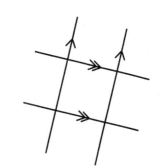

11 Two lines are perpendicular if they are at right angles to each other.
A horizontal line and a vertical line are perpendicular to each other.

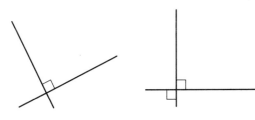

12 The shaded angles are equal.
They are called alternate angles (sometimes called 'Z' angles).

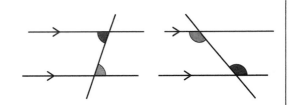

13 The shaded angles are equal.
They are called corresponding angles (sometimes called 'f' angles).

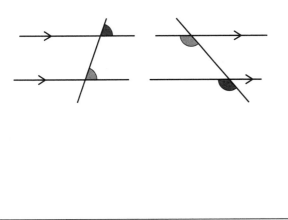

14 A bearing is an angle measured clockwise from North.
We use three digits, for example:
The bearing of *A* from *O* is 060°.
The bearing of *B* from *O* is 210°.

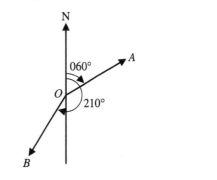

Worked examination question 1 [E]

PQ is a horizontal line.

On the diagram mark

(a)   a different horizontal line with a letter *H*
(b)   an acute angle with a letter *A*
(c)   an obtuse angle with a letter *O*.

Answer

(a)   Using ◼10
(b)   Using ◼3
(c)   Using ◼4

Note: an angle which is greater than a half turn is called a *reflex angle*.

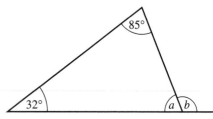

Example 1

Calculate the size of angle *a* and angle *b* in the diagram.
Give a reason for your answer.

Answer

To find *a*:

using ◼8, $32° + 85° + a = 180°$
$\qquad$ so $117° + a = 180°$
$\qquad\qquad a = 180° - 117°$
$\qquad\qquad a = 63°$ Angles in a triangle add up to 180°.

To find *b*:

using ◼5, $a + b = 180°$
$\qquad 63° + b = 180°$
$\qquad\qquad b = 180° - 63°$
$\qquad\qquad b = 117°$ Angles on a straight line equal 180°.

Example 2

Calculate the size of angles *x* and *y* in the diagram.

Answer

To find *x*:

using ◼9, $90° + 65° + 162° + x = 360°$
$\qquad\qquad 317° + x = 360°$
$\qquad\qquad\qquad x = 360° - 317°$
$\qquad\qquad\qquad x = 43°$

To find *y*:

using ◼7, angle $y =$ angle x (vertically opposite angles)
$\qquad$ angle $y = 43°$

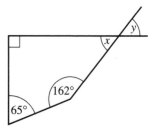

Example 3

Find the size of the angle marked with a letter.
Give a reason for your answer.
Using ⓬ $a = 48°$
a is the alternate angle to $48°$

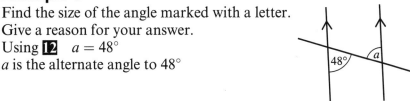

Worked examination question 2 [E]

Here is part of a plan of a small town.
In which compass direction is
(i)   the post office from the cinema
(ii) the cinema from the church?

Answer

Using ❶
(i)   East
(ii) South-west

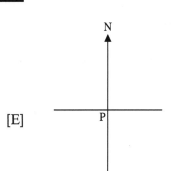

Revision exercise 16

1 John is standing at P. He is facing North.
He turns clockwise through 2 right angles.
(a) In what direction is he now facing?

Karen is standing at P. She is facing North.
She turns clockwise through 1 right angle.
(b) In what direction is she now facing?   [E]

2 Here is a map.

(a) Name the town north of Manchester.
(b) Name the town south west of Birmingham.   [E]

3 Using the diagram in question 2, measure:
  (a) the bearing of Norwich from London
  (b) the bearing of London from Birmingham.

4 (a) Measure and write down the size of angle ABC.

A

B   *C*

Copy the diagram accurately.
D is the point such that angle BCD is 102° and angle BAD is 68°.
  (b) Mark the position of D on the diagram and measure the angle
      at D.   [E]

5 The diagram shows the positions of some of the places
in Kim's village.
  (a) Which place is south west of the cinema?

Kim walked from her house to school.
  (b) In which compass direction did she walk?

Kim then walked from school to the church.
  (c) In which compass direction did she walk?   [E]

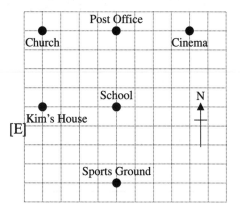

6 Find the angles represented by letters in these questions.
Give a reason for your answer.

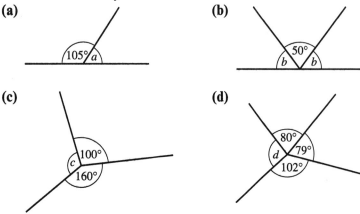

(a)   (b)

105° a   50°
                           b   b

(c)   (d)

c 100°   80°
  160°   d   79°
                             102°

(e)

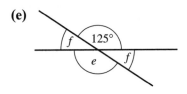

(f)

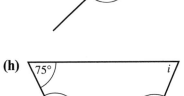

(g)

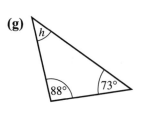

(h)

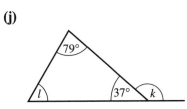

(i)

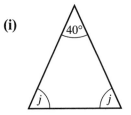

(j)

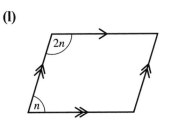

(k)

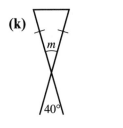

(l)

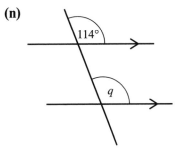

(m)

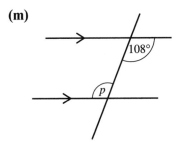

(n)

(o)

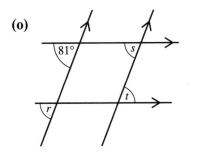

(p)

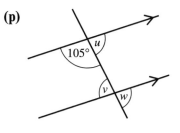

Test yourself	**What to review**

If your answer is incorrect, review Foundation book:

1 Alan is walking West. Which direction will he be facing when he turns a quarter turn anticlockwise?

Unit 3, Example 1
Unit 3, Example 1

---

2 What type of angle is at G?

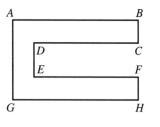

Unit 3, Section 3.2
Unit 3, Section 3.2

---

3 In the diagram for question 2, what line is parallel to AB?

Unit 3, Section 3.9
Unit 3, Section 3.9

---

4 Find the angles represented by *a*, *b* and *c*.
Give reasons for your answers.

Unit 3, Examples 6 and 7
Unit 3, Examples 6 and 7

---

5 Work out the missing angle *x*.

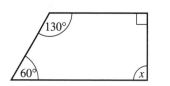

Unit 3, Example 8
Unit 3, Example 8

Test yourself answers

1 South   **2** right angle   **3** DC or EF or GH   **4** $a = 120°$, $b = 60°$, $c = 70°$: angles on a straight line add up to $180°$ **5** $80°$

17 3-D shapes

Key points to remember

1 A cube has:
- 6 square faces
- 12 edges
- 8 vertices

edge — vertex

face

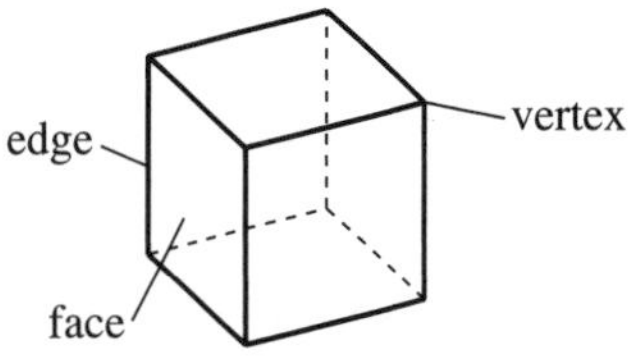

2 A cuboid has:
- 6 rectangular faces
- 12 edges
- 8 vertices

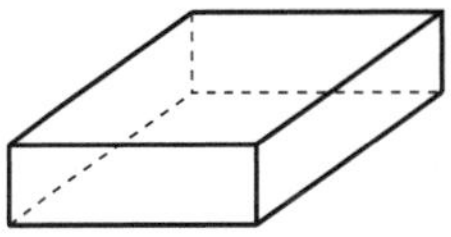

3 A sphere has:
- 1 curved face
- no edges
- no vertices

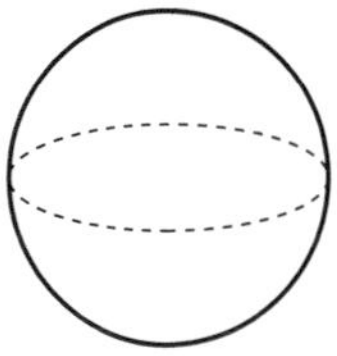

4 A square-based pyramid has:
- 1 square base and 4 triangular faces
- 8 edges
- 5 vertices

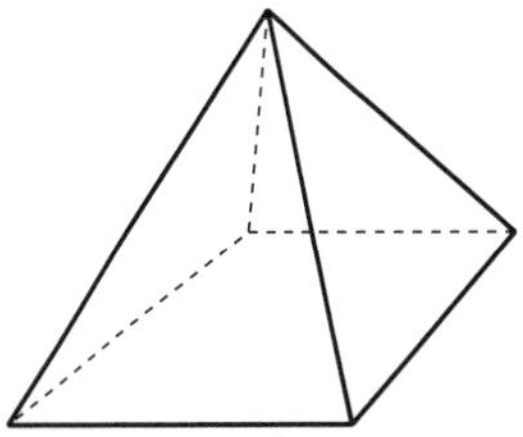

5 A triangular-based pyramid (tetrahedron) has:
- 4 triangular faces
- 6 edges
- 4 vertices

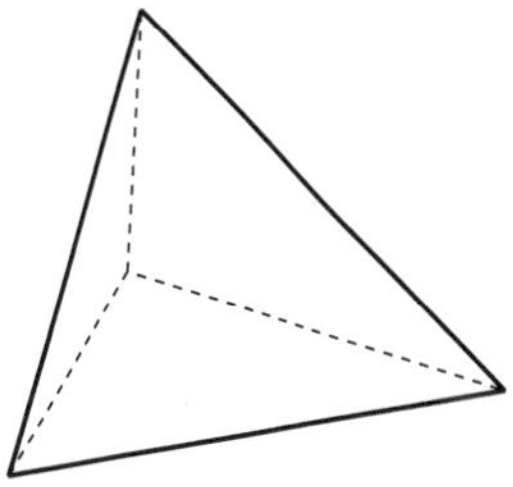

6 A cone has:
- 1 circular base and 1 curved face
- 1 circular edge
- 1 vertex

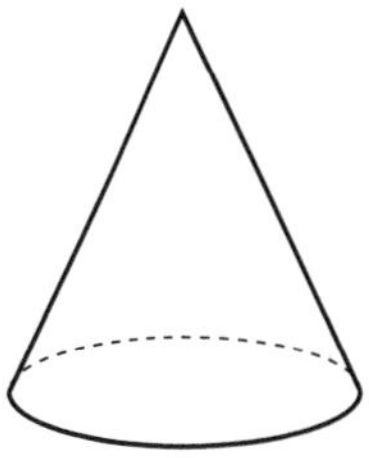

7 A cylinder has:
- 2 circular faces and 1 curved face
- 2 circular edges
- no vertices

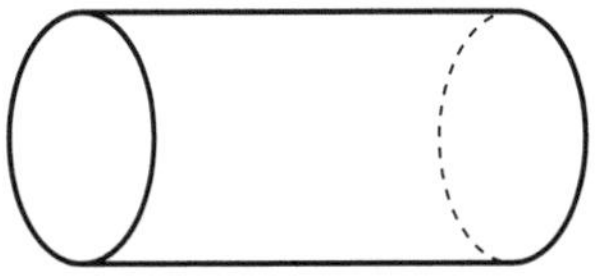

8 A prism is a shape whose cross-section is the same all the way through.

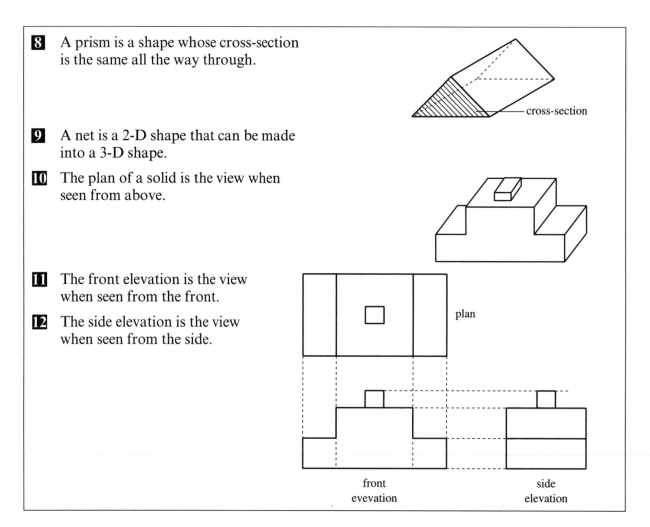

cross-section

9 A net is a 2-D shape that can be made into a 3-D shape.

10 The plan of a solid is the view when seen from above.

11 The front elevation is the view when seen from the front.

12 The side elevation is the view when seen from the side.

plan

front
evevation

side
elevation

Example 1

Draw the net of this cuboid.
Label the sides with the lengths.

Answer

Using **9**

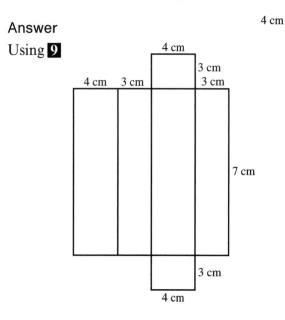

Example 2

Sketch the plan and elevations
of this shape.

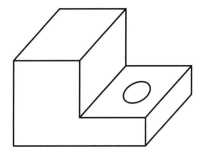

Using **10**, **11**, **12**

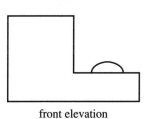

plan

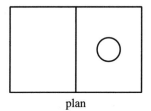

front elevation   side elevation

Revision exercise 17

1 Which of the following shapes are prisms?

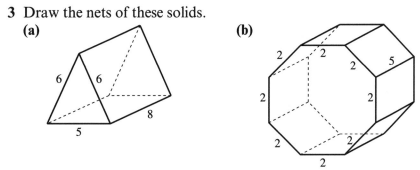

2 Draw the net of a cuboid that measures 2 cm by 5 cm by 6 cm.

3 Draw the nets of these solids.

(a)   **(b)**

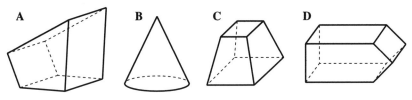

(c) Sketch the plans and elevations of the solids **(a)** and **(b)**.

4 The sketches show a
square-based pyramid
and its net.
The sides of the square
base and the height AB
are all 4 cm.

Use a ruler and
compasses to complete
the net accurately,
full size.

B

4 cm

A

4 cm   4 cm

A

Test yourself   # What to review

If your answer is incorrect,
review Foundation book:

1 (a) Sketch the solid from the net
below.
(b) Sketch the plans and elevations
of this solid.

Unit 11, Section 11.5
Unit 11, Section 11.5
Unit 11, Section 11.6
Unit 11, Section 11.6

---

2 Name the solid shape drawn in question 1.

Unit 11, Section 11.4
Unit 11, Section 11.4

Test yourself answers

1 (a)   **(b)**

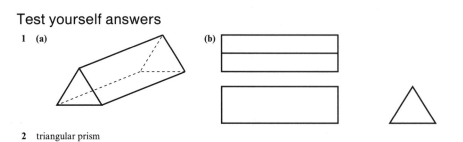

2 triangular prism

18 Perimeter, area and volume

Key points to remember

1 The perimeter of a shape is the distance around the edge of the shape.

2 The perimeter of a circle is called the circumference.
$C = \pi \times \text{diameter}$
$\quad = 2 \times \pi \times \text{radius}$
The value of pi (π) is approximately 3.14
You may have a more accurate value on your calculator.

3 You can estimate area by counting squares.

4 Area of a rectangle = length $\times$ width.

5 Area of a triangle = $\frac{1}{2} \times$ base $\times$ vertical height.

6 Area of a parallelogram = base $\times$ vertical height

7 Area of a circle, $A = \pi \times r^2$ or $\pi \times r \times r$.

8 Volume of a cuboid = length $\times$ width $\times$ height.

9 Volume of a prism = area of base $\times$ length.

10 $1\,m^2 = 100 \times 100\,cm^2 = 10\,000\,cm^2$

11 $1\,m^3 = 100 \times 100 \times 100\,cm^3 = 1\,000\,000\,cm^3$

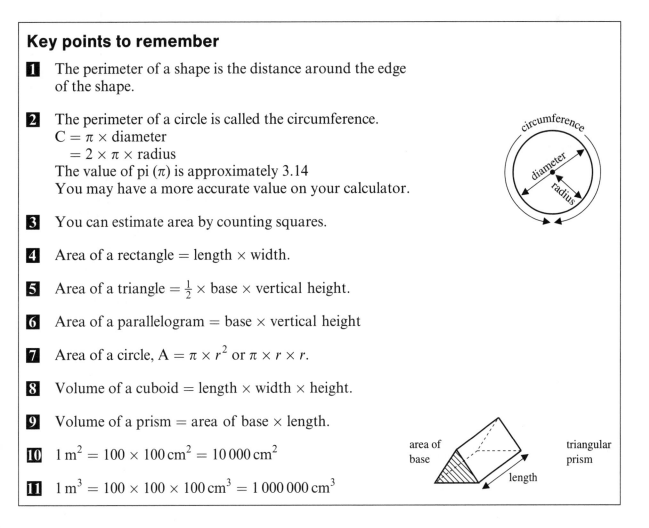

Worked examination question 1 [E]

The diagram shows the measurements, in inches, of the 'L' on an 'L' plate.
(a) Work out the perimeter of the 'L'.
(b) Work out the area of the 'L'.

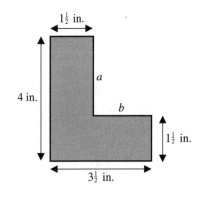

Answer

(a) Missing sides $a = 4 - 1\frac{1}{2} = 2\frac{1}{2}$ inches
$\qquad\qquad\quad b = 3\frac{1}{2} - 1\frac{1}{2} = 2$ inches

Using **1**, perimeter $= 2\frac{1}{2} + 2 + 1\frac{1}{2} + 3\frac{1}{2} + 4 + 1\frac{1}{2}$
$\qquad\qquad\qquad\qquad = 15$ inches

(b) Divide the 'L' into two rectangles
X = 4 by $1\frac{1}{2}$
Y = 2 by $1\frac{1}{2}$
Using **4**
Area X = $4 \times 1\frac{1}{2} = 6$
Area Y = $2 \times 1\frac{1}{2} = 3$
Total area = $6 + 3 = 9$ square inches

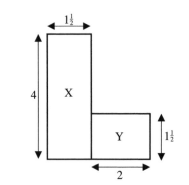

Worked examination question 2 [E]
The diagram shows a **circular** garden pond.
The radius of the pond is 120 cm.
(a) Calculate to the nearest 10 cm,
the circumference of the pond.
(b) Calculate to the nearest 10 cm^2
the area of the pond.

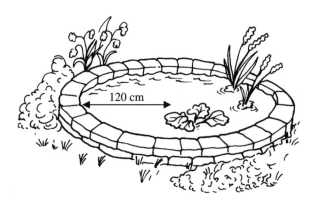

Answer

(a) Using **2**, circumference = $2 \times \pi \times$ radius
$= 2 \times \pi \times 120$
$= 753.98$
$= 750$ cm to nearest 10 cm

(b) Using **7**, area = $\pi \times r \times r$
$= \pi \times 120 \times 120$
$= 45\,238.9$
$= 45\,240$ cm^2 to nearest 10 cm^2

Worked examination question 3 [E]
The diagram represents the net of a box without a lid.
(a) Calculate the total area of the net.
(b) Calculate the volume of the box.

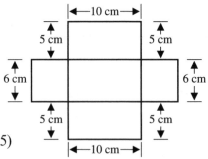

Answer

(a) The net is made up of 5 rectangles
Using **4**,
area of net = $(6 \times 5) + (6 \times 5) + (10 \times 5) + (10 \times 6) + (10 \times 5)$
$= 30 + 30 + 50 + 60 + 50$
$= 220$ cm^2

(b) Folded up the box looks like this.
Here length = 10 cm
width = 6 cm
height = 5 cm
Using **8**, volume = length × width × height
$= 10 \times 6 \times 5$
$= 300$ cm^3

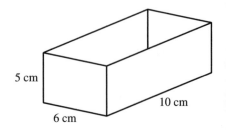

Revision exercise 18

1 (a) Find the area, in cm², of the shape.
  (b) Find the perimeter, in cm, of the shape.   [E]

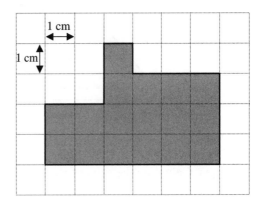

2 Find the area and perimeter of this shape.

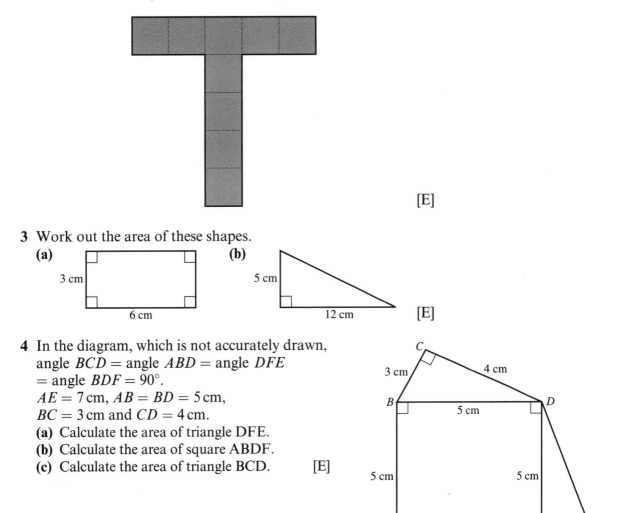

[E]

3 Work out the area of these shapes.

(a) 3 cm 6 cm

(b) 5 cm 12 cm   [E]

4 In the diagram, which is not accurately drawn,
  angle BCD = angle ABD = angle DFE
  = angle $BDF = 90°$.
  $AE = 7$ cm, $AB = BD = 5$ cm,
  $BC = 3$ cm and $CD = 4$ cm.
  (a) Calculate the area of triangle DFE.
  (b) Calculate the area of square ABDF.
  (c) Calculate the area of triangle BCD.   [E]

C 3 cm 4 cm
B 5 cm D
5 cm 5 cm
2 cm
A F E

5

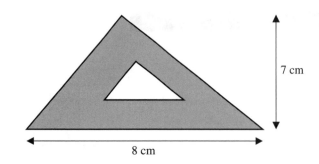

In the diagram, the outer triangle has base 8 cm and height 7 cm.

(a) Calculate the area of the outer triangle.

The base and height of the inner triangle are each half those of the outer triangle.

(b) Calculate the area of the inner triangle.

(c) Hence, calculate the area of the shaded part.   [E]

6 An earthquake has its centre at the centre of the circle shown in the scale drawing and affects everywhere inside the circle.

(a) Find the actual radius, in kilometres, of the circle affected by the earthquake.

(b) Calculate the area affected by the earthquake. Give your answer in km^2 correct to the nearest whole number.   [E]

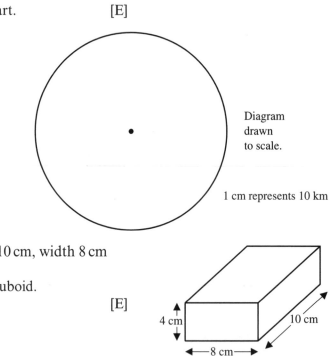

Diagram drawn to scale.

1 cm represents 10 km

7 The diagram represents a cuboid of length 10 cm, width 8 cm and height 4 cm.

(a) Work out the area of the top face of the cuboid.

(b) Work out the volume of the cuboid.   [E]

8 A circular carpet has a diameter of 3.2 m.
What is the **(a)** circumference **(b)** area?

9 The diagram shows a box for an Easter egg.
The box is in the shape of a triangular prism.
The area of the top of the box is $40 \, cm^2$.
The box is 20 cm high.

(a) Calculate the volume of the box.

The Easter egg takes up 45% of the volume of the box. The rest of the box is empty space.

(b) Calculate the volume of empty space in the box.   [E]

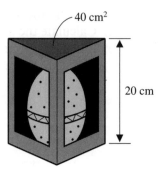

40 cm²

20 cm

10 The area of a door is $25\,000\,\text{cm}^2$.
Work out the area of 20 doors.
Give your answer in m^2.

11 The volume of a chest is $1.2\,\text{m}^2$.
Write the volume of the chest in cm^3.

Test yourself	What to review

If your answer is incorrect,
review Foundation book:

1 (a) Work out the perimeter of the rectangle.

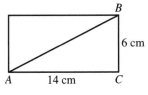

Unit 19, Example 1
Unit 19, Example 1

(b) Work out the area of triangle ABC.

Unit 19, Example 7(c)
Unit 19, Example 7(c)

(c) Work out the area of the rectangle.

Unit 19, Example 7(a)
Unit 19, Example 7(a)

2 (a) Work out the perimeter of this circle.

Unit 19, Example 3
Unit 19, Example 3

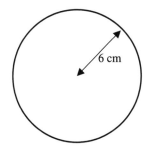

(b) Work out the area of this circle.

Unit 19, Examples 10 and 11
Unit 19, Examples 10 and 11

3 A cuboid measures $3\,\text{cm} \times 6\,\text{cm} \times 8\,\text{cm}$.
Work out the volume.

Unit 19, Example 12
Unit 19, Example 12

4 The volume of a chest freezer is $1.8\,\text{m}^3$.
Write down the volume in cm^3.

Unit 19, Section 9.6
Unit 19, Section 9.6

Test yourself answers

1 (a) 40 cm (b) 42 cm^2 (c) 84 cm^2 **2** (a) 37.7 cm (b) 113.1 cm^2 **3** 144 cm^3

19 Symmetry

Key points to remember

1 A 2-D shape has a line of symmetry if the line divides the shape into two halves and one half is the mirror image of the other half.

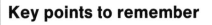

line of symmetry or mirror line

2 A 2-D shape with rotational symmetry repeats the appearance of its starting position two or more times during a full turn.

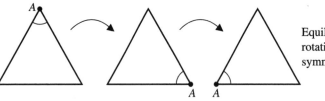

Equilateral triangle, rotational symmetry order 3.

3 The order of rotational symmetry is the number of times the original appearance is repeated in a full turn.

4 Regular polygons have the same number of lines of symmetry as they have sides.

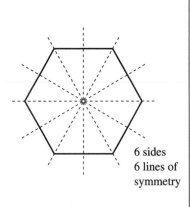

6 sides
6 lines of symmetry

5 The order of rotational symmetry of a regular polygon is the same as the number of sides.
So a regular hexagon has rotational symmetry, order 6.

6 A plane of symmetry separates a 3-D shape into two halves which are mirror images of each other.

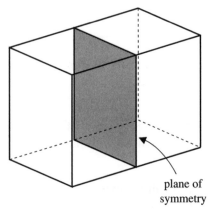

plane of symmetry

Worked examination question 1 [E]

Each of the shapes below has at least one line of symmetry.
Draw all the lines of symmetry on these shapes.

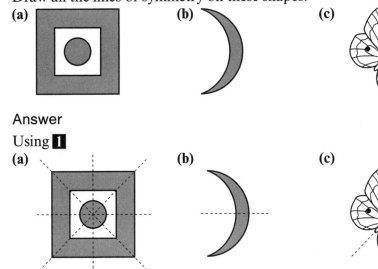

(a)   **(b)**   **(c)**

Answer

Using ▮**1**

(a)   **(b)**   **(c)**

Worked examination question 2 [E]

The diagram represents a prism.
The cross-section (shaded region) of the
prism is a right-angled isosceles triangle.
Draw one plane of symmetry of the prism.

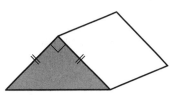

Answer

Using ▮**6**

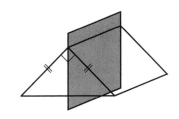

Revision exercise 19

1 **(a)**   **(b)**   **(c)**   **(d)**

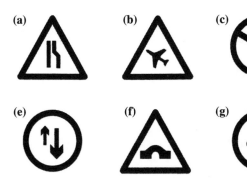

(e)   **(f)**   **(g)**   **(g)**

Which of these signs have line symmetry?   [E]

2 Copy and draw all the lines of symmetry of this shape.

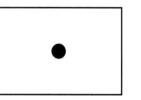

[E]

3 Here are 4 shapes labelled A to D.

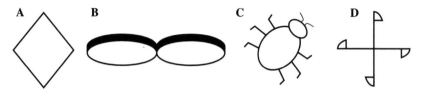

(a) Copy and draw in any lines of symmetry on the shapes.
(b) Write TRUE and FALSE for each of the following statements.
  (i)   Shape A has rotational symmetry of order 2 or more.
  (ii) Shape B has rotational symmetry of order 2 or more.
  (iii) Shape C has rotational symmetry of order 2 or more.
  (iv) Shape D has rotational symmetry of order 2 or more.

4 Copy or trace the shapes below. Show the plane or planes of symmetry on your diagram.

(a)   (b)

5

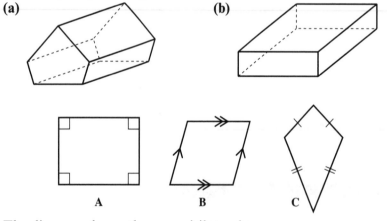

The diagram shows three quadrilaterals.
(a) (i)   Write down the letter of the quadrilateral with exactly **one** line of symmetry.
    (ii) Write down the mathematical name of this quadrilateral.
(b) (i)   Write down the letter of the quadrilateral with rotational symmetry of order 2 **and** two lines of symmetry.
    (ii) Write down the mathematical name of this quadrilateral.
(c) (i)   Write down the letter of the quadrilateral with rotational symmetry of order 2 but **no** lines of symmetry.
    (ii) Write down the mathematical name of this quadrilateral.

[E]

6 Write down the letter of each of the shapes that have rotational symmetry.

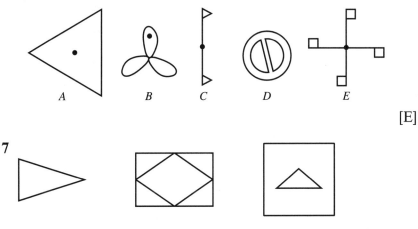

[E]

7

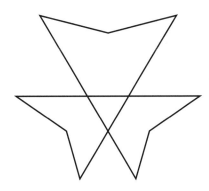

Copy the shapes and draw in all the lines of symmetry for each one. [E]

8

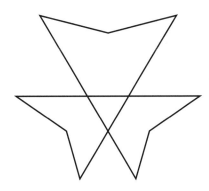

(a) Write down the order of rotational symmetry of the shape.
(b) Copy the diagram and label
   (i)   an acute angle with a letter A,
   (ii) an obtuse angle with a letter B,
   (iii) a reflex angle with a letter C. [E]

Test yourself	**What to review**
	If your answer is incorrect, review Foundation book:
1 Copy and draw all the lines of symmetry for this shape.	*Unit 18, Section 18.1*
	Unit 18, Section 18.1

Test yourself	What to review

If your answer is incorrect,
review Foundation book:

2 What is the order of rotational symmetry for this shape?

Unit 18, Examples 2 and 3
Unit 18, Examples 2 and 3

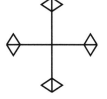

3 How many planes of symmetry has a cuboid?

Unit 18, Example 4
Unit 18, Example 4

Test yourself answers

1

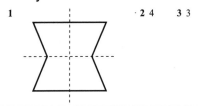

·**2** 4   **3** 3

20 Transformations

Key points to remember

1 Sliding movements are called translations.

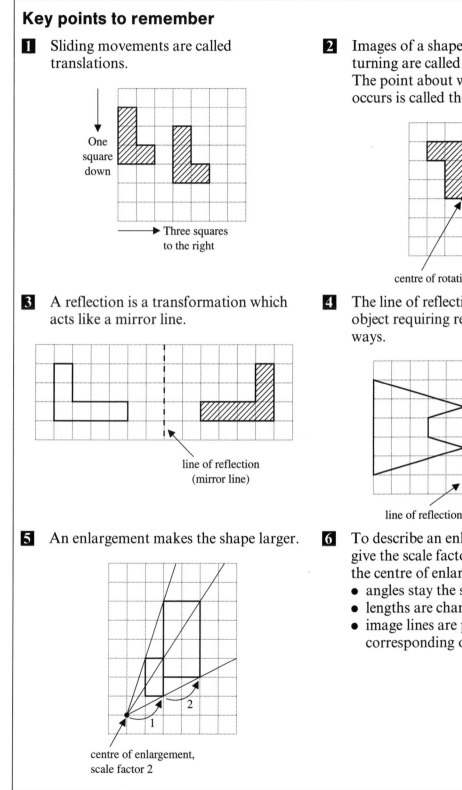

One square down

Three squares to the right

2 Images of a shape which are formed by turning are called rotations of the shape. The point about which the turning occurs is called the centre of rotation.

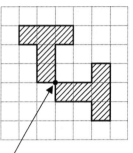

centre of rotation

3 A reflection is a transformation which acts like a mirror line.

line of reflection (mirror line)

4 The line of reflection may go through the object requiring reflection to go both ways.

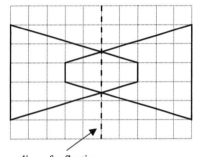

line of reflection

5 An enlargement makes the shape larger.

centre of enlargement, scale factor 2

6 To describe an enlargement you need to give the scale factor of enlargement and the centre of enlargement.
- angles stay the same
- lengths are changed by the scale factor
- image lines are parallel to their corresponding object lines.

7 A pattern of shapes which fit together without leaving any gaps or overlapping is called a tessellation.

Worked examination question 1 [E]
Reflect this shape in the mirror line given.

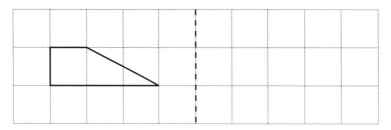

Answer
Using **3**

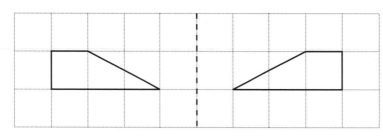

Worked examination question 2 [E]
On a grid enlarge the shaded shape by a scale factor of 3.
Start your enlargement at point B.

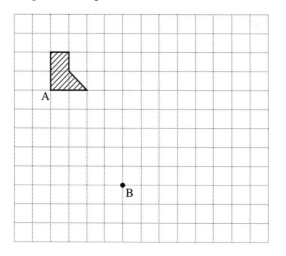

Answer

Using

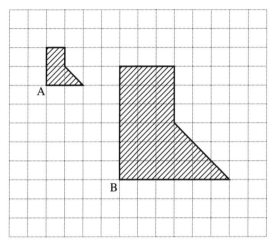

Each line is 3 times the original length. All the corresponding angles are equal.

Example 1

Describe the translation for the shape opposite.

Answer

Using **1**, translation is 1 square down and 4 squares to the right.

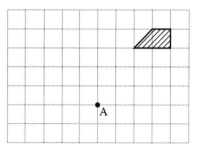

Revision exercise 20

1 On a copy of the grid enlarge the shape by a scale factor of 2. Start at point A.

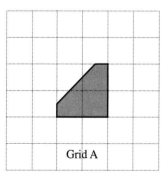

2 (a) Copy the grid and draw a line of symmetry of the shaded shape on Grid A.
  (b) On a 10 by 10 square grid draw an enlargement, scale factor 3, of the shaded shape.   [E]

3

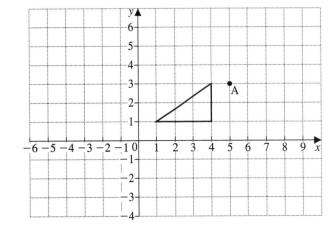

Copy the diagram above.
Rotate the triangle through 180° about centre A.
On the grid draw the new position of the triangle. [E]

4

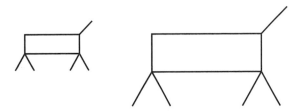

One drawing is an enlargement of the other.
(a) Copy the diagram and find the centre of enlargement.
 Label this point C.
(b) State the scale factor of the enlargement.

5 Copy and reflect each shape in the mirror line given.

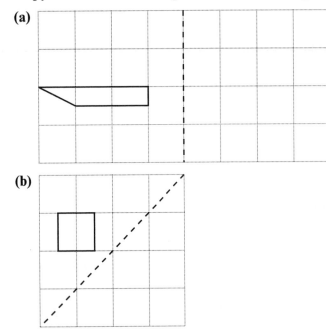

(a)

(b)

6 (a) Copy the grid then
     (i)   plot the points B(4, 3) and C(3, 6)
     (ii) join A, B and C to make a triangle.

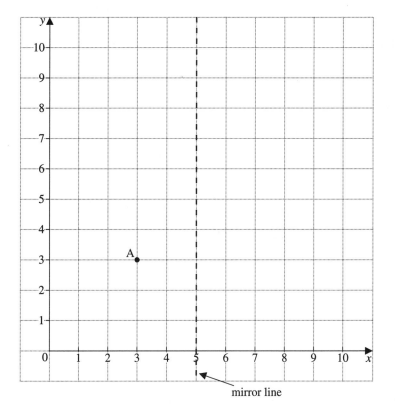

mirror line

(b) Copy the grid and draw the reflection of triangle ABC in the mirror line.

(c) Choose three descriptions from the box to complete the sentence correctly.
Triangle ABC and its reflections are .... , and
....   [E]

scalene
isosceles
right angled
equilateral
acute angled
obtuse angled
congruent

7 The drawing shows the left side of a pattern made from a sequence of triangles.
The right side of the pattern is a reflection, in the mirror line, of the left side.

(a) Copy the diagram and draw the right side of the pattern.

(b) The triangles in the sequence are getting larger.
Explain what size the next triangle in the sequence would be.

(c) Comment on what you notice about the areas of each triangle in the sequence.   [E]

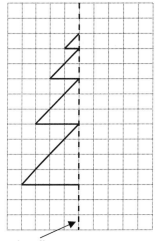

mirror line

Test yourself

If your answer is incorrect,
review Foundation book:

1 Describe the transformation which
maps triangle A on to triangle B.

Unit 22, Example 1
Unit 22, Example 1

2 Draw the image of the shape
after it has been rotated 90°
clockwise about centre O.

Unit 22, Example 2
Unit 22, Example 2

3 Enlarge the shape by scale factor 2.
Start at point A.

Unit 22, Section 22.4
Unit 22, Section 22.4

Test yourself answers

1   1 up and 4 backwards (4 to the left)   **2** 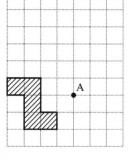   **3**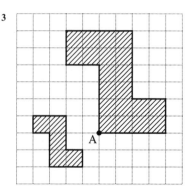

21 Probability

Probability uses numbers to represent how likely or unlikely it is that an event will happen.

Key points to remember

1 An event which is certain to happen has a probability of 1.

2 An event which cannot happen has a probability of 0.

3 The probability of an event happening is always
$0 \leqslant \text{Probability} \leqslant 1$

Remember:
$\leqslant$ means less than or equal to
$\geqslant$ means greater than or equal to

4 The probability that something will happen is
$$\text{Probability} = \frac{\text{number of successful outcomes}}{\text{total number of possible outcomes}}$$
assuming the outcomes are equally likely.

5 If the probability of an event happening is p then the probability of it **not** happening is $1 - p$.

6 The estimated probability that an event will happen in a game or experiment is
$$\text{Estimated probability} = \frac{\text{number of successful trials}}{\text{total number of trials}}$$
The estimated probability is called the relative frequency that the event will happen.

7 Sample space diagrams, tree diagrams and two-way tables can be used to help identify combinations of outcomes.

Worked examination question 1 [E]

```
├──────────────────────────────────┤
0                                   1
```

A dice is rolled.
(a) On the scale, mark with a **G** the probability that a number greater than 7 will be scored.
(b) On the scale, mark with an **L** the probability that a number less than 7 will be scored.

Answer

```
  G                                 L
  ✕─────────────────────────────────✕
  0                                 1
```

(a) Using **2**, Probability $= 0$
(b) Using **1**, Probability $= 1$

Worked examination question 2 [E]

A game is played with two spinners. They are spun at the same time. The result shown is Blue 3.

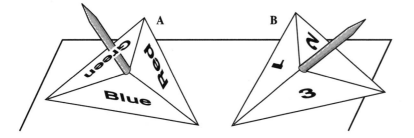

(a) List all the possible results when the spinners are spun.

Spinner A is a fair spinner.
(b) What is the probability of not getting green with spinner A?

Spinner B is weighted (biased). The probability of getting a 3 is 0.2 and the probability of getting a 1 is 0.3.
(c) What is the probability of getting a 2 with spinner B?

Answer

(a) Using **7**, space diagram

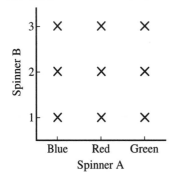

Reading points from the space diagram, the outcomes are:

Blue 1, Blue 2, Blue 3, Red 1, Red 2, Red 3, Green 1, Green 2, Green 3.

(b) Using **4**, Prob(Green) $= \frac{1}{3}$
Using **5**, Prob(Not Green) $= 1 - \frac{1}{3}$
$$= \frac{2}{3}$$

(c) Prob(3 or 1) $= 0.2 + 0.3$
$$= 0.5$$
Using **5**, Prob(2) $= 1 - 0.5$
$$= 0.5$$

Revision exercise 21

1 To play a game you spin the pointer.
You win the prize on which the pointer stops.
Richard has one spin.

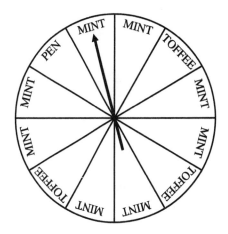

(a) Which prize is Richard most likely to win?
(b) Explain your answer to part **(a)**.

Donna has one spin.

(c) Copy the line below and mark with a P the probability that
Donna will win a pen.

$$0 \qquad \tfrac{1}{2} \qquad 1$$

(d) Copy the line below and mark with a W the
probability that Donna will win a watch.

$$0 \qquad \tfrac{1}{2} \qquad 1$$

[E]

2

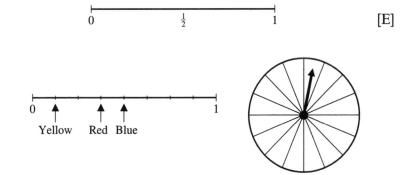

In a game you spin an arrow. The arrow stops on one of sixteen
equal sectors of a circle. Each sector of the circle is coloured.
The probability scale shows how likely it should be for the
arrow to stop on any one colour.

Copy and shade these circles to show how many sectors
should be
(a) coloured red   **(b)** coloured blue.

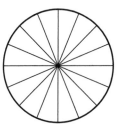
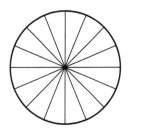

[E]

3 A game in an amusement arcade can show the following pictures. The fraction under each picture shows the probability of the picture being shown at the first window.

Cherry	Bar	Banana	Strawberry	Apple
$\frac{4}{12}$	$\frac{1}{12}$	$\frac{2}{12}$	$\frac{2}{12}$	$\frac{3}{12}$

Calculate the probability of the game **not** showing a Bar at the first window.   [E]

4 Peter and Asif are both taking their driving test for a motor cycle for the first time.
The table below gives the probabilities that they will pass the test at their first attempt.

	Probability of passing at first attempt
Peter	0.6
Asif	0.7

(a) Write down the probability that Asif will pass the test at the first attempt.
(b) Work out the probability that Peter will fail the test at the first attempt.
(c) Explain clearly why Asif is more likely to pass the test at the first attempt than he is to fail at the first attempt.   [E]

5 A newspaper article states that the probability of winning the National Lottery jackpot prize with one £1 ticket is $\frac{1}{14\,000\,000}$.

Using this figure, what is the probability, with one £1 ticket, of **not** winning the National Lottery jackpot?

6 Work out the probability of
(a) getting a head when a pound coin is thrown,
(b) getting a 5 when an ordinary dice is thrown,
(c) pulling out a ball numbered 10 when a ball is drawn at random from a bag containing 49 balls numbered 1–49.   [E]

7 Two fair spinners are used in a game.
The first spinner is labelled 1, 1, 2, 3.
The second spinner is labelled 2, 3, 4, 5.
Both spinners are spun. The **score** is the positive difference between the numbers shown.

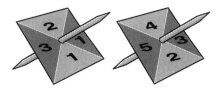

(a) Copy and complete the table to show the possible scores.

		second spinner			
		2	3	4	5
first spinner	1	1	2	3	4
	1	1			
	2	0			
	3	1			

(b) What is the most likely score? [E]

8 A fair dice has the numbers 1 to 6 on it.

(a) When the dice is rolled, what is the probability that a 4 will be scored?

A fair spinner has the numbers 1, 2 and 3 on it.

(b) When the spinner is spun, what is the probability that a 3 will be scored?

In a game, the dice is rolled and the spinner is spun. The two scores are added.

(c) Copy and complete the table to show all the possible totals.

Dice \ Spinner	1	2	3
1			
2			
3			
4			
5			
6			

(d) What is the probability that a total of 4 will be scored?

A fair spinner with the numbers 1, 2, 3 and 4 on it is used in the game instead of the 3-sided spinner.

(e) Will there be an increase or decrease in the probability that a total of 4 will be scored? Explain your answer. [E]

9 A packet contains only yellow counters and green counters.
There are 8 yellow counters and 5 green counters.
A counter is to be taken at random from the packet.

(a) Write down the probability that
   (i) a yellow counter will be taken,
   (ii) a yellow counter will **not** be taken.

A second counter is to be taken from the packet.

(b) Write down all the possible outcomes of taking two counters from the packet. [E]

Test yourself

What to review

If your answer is incorrect, review Foundation book:

1 A five-sided fair spinner is spun.

(a) Mark with an A on a probability line the probability of getting a two.

Unit 23, Section 23.1
Unit 23, Section 23.1

(b) What is the probability of getting a 4?

Unit 23, Example 1
Unit 23, Example 1

(c) What is the probability of not getting a 4?

Unit 23, Section 23.4
Unit 23, Section 23.4

A coin is tossed and the spinner spun.

(d) List all the possible outcomes.

Unit 23, Example 4
Unit 23, Example 4

Test yourself answers

1 (a)  (b) $\frac{1}{5}$ (c) $\frac{4}{5}$

(d) (Head, 1) (Head, 2) (Head, 3) (Head, 4) (Head, 5) (Tail, 1) (Tail, 2) (Tail, 3) (Tail, 4) (Tail, 5)

22 Collecting, recording and interpreting data

Key points to remember

1 When designing questions to collect data for a questionnaire
   (a) be clear what you want to find out, and what data you need
   (b) ask short simple questions
   (c) avoid questions which are too vague, too personal or which may influence the answer.

2 When you carry out a survey select a random sample to avoid bias.

3 When you collect data from experiments use a data capture sheet, for example:

Type of vehicle	Tally
Car	ⵏ II
Bus	II
Lorry	III
Bike	ⵏ ⵏ II
Motorbike	III

ⵏ = 5 items

4 Data you collect is called primary data. Data that may have been collected by other people is called secondary data.

Worked examination question [E]

Fred is conducting a survey into television viewing habits. One of the questions in his survey is 'How much television do you watch?' His friend Sheila tells him that it is not a very good question. Write down two ways in which Fred could improve his question.

Answer

Using **1**
1 Indicate a period of time, for example: 'in a week' or 'in a day'.
2 Include tick boxes to select the number of hours, for example:

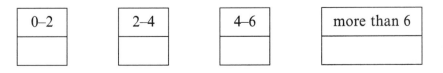

0–2	2–4	4–6	more than 6

Revision exercise 22

1 This table shows the marks for 5 pupils.
   (a) Write down the name of the pupil who
       has the highest Maths mark.
   (b) Write down the name of the pupil who
       has the lowest English mark.
   (c) Write down the name of the pupil who
       has two marks of 30.   [E]

Name	Maths	English	Science
Senga	24	26	28
Omar	25	30	26
Samantha	28	15	20
Ihab	15	28	30
Morag	30	23	30

2 The fuel consumption of cars is measured in miles per gallon
   (mpg). The table gives information about the fuel consumption
   of different makes of car.

	Make of car					
	Audi	Citroen	Ford	Peugeot	Rover	Vauxhall
Fuel consumption						
Urban cycle (mpg)	44.1	37.2	39.2	34.0	48.4	42.2
56 mph (mpg)	70.6	56.5	62.8	55.4	70.3	61.4
75 mph (mpg)	51.4	41.5	44.1	41.5	51.7	44.8

   (a) What is the fuel consumption at 56 mph for the Ford?
   (b) Which make of car has the highest figure for the urban cycle?
                                                          [E]

3 A travel agent has printed out details of holidays in August.

Complex	Hotel	Children's Club	Price	
			7 nights	14 nights
Alcudia	Bahia	No	£489	£599
Alcudia	Pins	Yes	£299	£399
Alcudia	Siesta	Yes	£309	£379
Picafort	Tonga	No	£379	£569
S'illot	Arcos Playa	No	£249	£369
Sa Coma	Bougavilla Park	Yes	£304	£389
Calas	Eurocalas	No	£329	£499
Santa Ponsa	Punta del Mar	No	£409	£419
Santa Ponsa	Jardin del Sol	No	£309	£419

   (a) Write down the name of the hotel at complex Picafort.
   (b) Which hotels have 7-night holidays for under £300?
   (c) Which hotels have 14-night holidays costing between £320 and
       £390, and also have a children's club?   [E]

4 Karl's and Eleanor's school is near a busy main road.
They decide to carry out a survey of the different types of
vehicles that travel on the main road.

Design a suitable data sheet so that they can collect their data
easily. [E]

5 Laurie is designing a survey to find out about people who use a
superstore near her home.
One of the things Laurie wants to find out is how far people
have travelled to get to the superstore.
  (a) Decide which question below is best to ask. Give two reasons
     for your decision.
     (A) How far have you travelled to get here today?
     (B) Where do you live?
     (C) Do you live far from here?
     (D) Please show me on this map where you have travelled
         from.
Laurie decides to do her survey one Friday evening outside the
superstore.
  (b) Give one reason why this would give a biased sample. [E]

Test yourself	**What to review**
	If your answer is incorrect, review Foundation book:
1 Draw up a questionnaire to find out the different types of television programmes people watch.	*Unit 8, Section 8.2, Example 1*
2 Tom asks the following question in a questionnaire, 'You like butter don't you?' Comment on this question.	*Unit 8, Section 8.2*

Test yourself answers

1 Data capture sheet with categories such as soaps, news, drama.   **2** The question is biased and leading asking you to say 'yes'. It is unfair.

23 Presenting data

Key points to remember

1 A tally chart can be used to display data that can be counted.

2 A bar chart can be used to display data that can be counted.

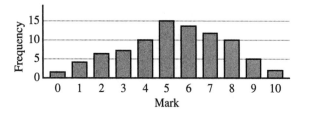

Data that can be counted is called discrete data.

Data that is weighed or measured is called continuous data.

3 A pictogram can be used to illustrate data that can be counted using symbols to represent amounts.

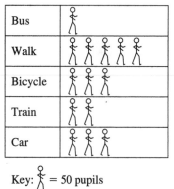

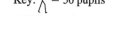

Key: 🚶 = 50 pupils

4 Pie charts are usually used to display information that can be counted. The angles at the centre of a pie chart add up to 360°.

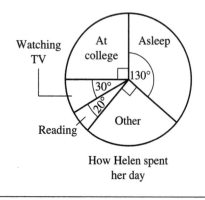

How Helen spent her day

5 Line graphs can be used to display continuous data.
They are used to show trends over a period of time.

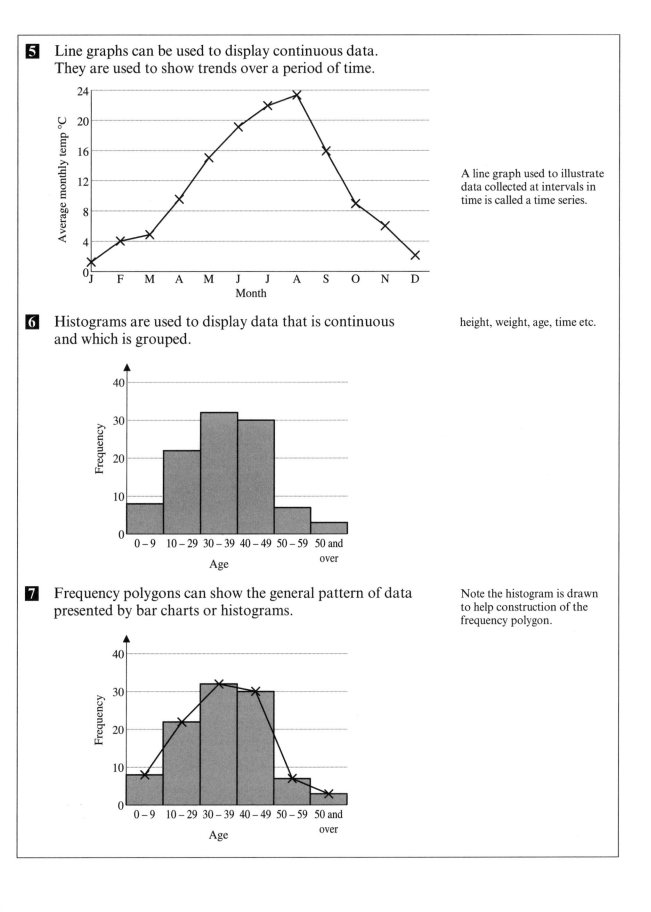

A line graph used to illustrate data collected at intervals in time is called a time series.

6 Histograms are used to display data that is continuous and which is grouped.

height, weight, age, time etc.

7 Frequency polygons can show the general pattern of data presented by bar charts or histograms.

Note the histogram is drawn to help construction of the frequency polygon.

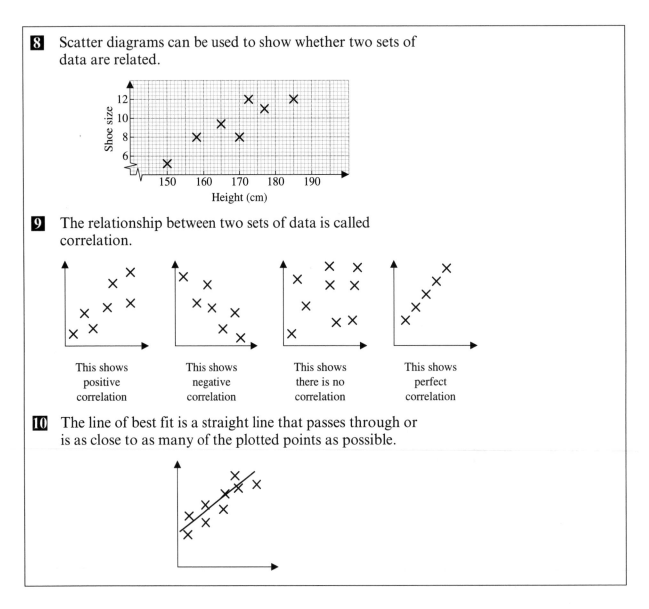

8 Scatter diagrams can be used to show whether two sets of data are related.

9 The relationship between two sets of data is called correlation.

This shows positive correlation

This shows negative correlation

This shows there is no correlation

This shows perfect correlation

10 The line of best fit is a straight line that passes through or is as close to as many of the plotted points as possible.

Worked examination question 1 [E]

As part of his Geography fieldwork, Tony took measurements of the steepness of slopes. The steepness was measured as the angle the slope made with the horizontal. Tony's results are shown below.

$$15°, \ 16°, \ \ 9°, \ 21°, \ 32°,$$
$$37°, \ 25°, \ 36°, \ 40°, \ \ 8°,$$
$$13°, \ 21°, \ 32°, \ 29°, \ 32°,$$
$$\ 7°, \ \ 4°, \ 18°, \ 17°, \ 32°,$$

Tony decided to group the data into 4 equal class intervals on an observation sheet.

(a) Copy and complete the observation sheet below, using 4 equal class intervals.

Class interval (steepness°)	Tally	Frequency
1–10		

(b) Use the completed observation sheet to draw a frequency diagram of the data.

Answer

(a) Using **1**,

Class interval (steepness°)	Tally	Frequency
1–10	||||	4
11–20	卌	5
21–30	||||	4
31–40	卌 ||	7

(b) Using **6**, the most sensible frequency diagram to draw is a histogram as the data is continuous (a measurement).

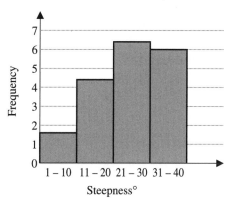

Worked examination question 2 [E]

300 young people were asked what they did after completing Year 11 at school. The pie chart shows the results of the survey.

(a) How many young people were working?

Gwen made an accurate drawing of the pie chart.
She first drew the sector representing the young people out of work.

(b) Calculate the size of the angle of this sector.
Give your answer correct to the nearest degree.

(c) Change to a decimal the percentage going to college.

(d) What fraction of the young people stayed at school?
Give your answer in its simplest form.

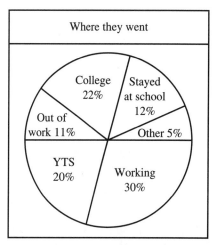

Diagram not accurately drawn

Answer

(a)   Working = 30% (from pie chart)
      30% of 300 = $\frac{30}{100} \times 300$
                  = 90 young people

(b)   Out of work = 11%
      Using **4**, a pie chart as 360°.
      Therefore 11% of 360° = $\frac{11}{100} \times 360$
                               = 39.6°
                               = 40° to nearest degree

(c)   Going to college = 22%
                       = $\frac{22}{100}$ = 22 ÷ 100 = 0.22

(d)   Stayed at school = 12%
                     = $\frac{12}{100} = \frac{3}{25}$

Worked examination question 3 [L]

The table lists the weights of twelve books and the number of pages in each one.

Number of pages	80	155	100	125	145	90	140	160	135	100	115	165
Weight (g)	160	330	200	260	320	180	290	330	260	180	230	350

(a)   Draw a scatter graph to show the information in the table.
(b)   Describe the correlation between the number of pages in these books and their weights.
(c)   Draw and label the line of best fit on your scatter diagram.

Answer

(a)   **8**,

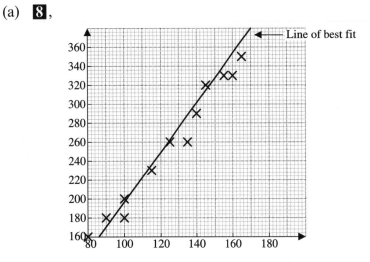

(b)   Using **9**, this scatter diagram shows positive correlation.
(c)   Using **10** see scatter diagram.

Revision exercise 23

1 The pictogram shows the number of golfers who played at
the local golf club last week.
(a) How many golfers played on Sunday?
(b) How many golfers played on Monday?
On Tuesday 35 golfers played.
(c) Copy and complete the pictogram to show this. [E]

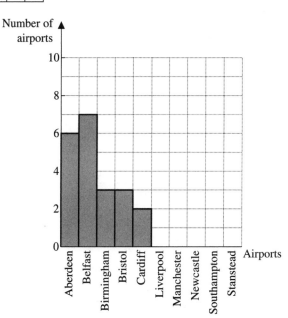

2 This table shows whether there is a direct flight between the
airports listed at the top and side of the diagram.

Key
● direct flight
☐ not a direct flight

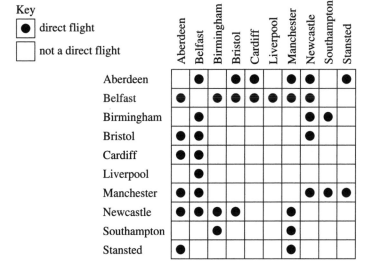

	Aberdeen	Belfast	Birmingham	Bristol	Cardiff	Liverpool	Manchester	Newcastle	Southampton	Stansted
Aberdeen		●		●	●		●	●		●
Belfast	●		●	●	●	●	●	●		
Birmingham		●						●	●	
Bristol	●	●					●			
Cardiff	●	●								
Liverpool		●								
Manchester	●	●						●	●	●
Newcastle	●	●	●	●			●			
Southampton			●				●			
Stansted	●						●			

(a) Is there a direct flight between these
airports? (Answer 'yes' or 'no'.)
Manchester and Aberdeen
Bristol and Cardiff
Birmingham and Newcastle
(b) (i) How many airports have a direct
flight from Stansted?
(ii) How many airports have a direct
flight from Manchester?
(c) The block graph opposite shows the
numbers of direct flights from some of
the airports. Copy and complete the
block graph for the rest of the 10 airports.
(d) From which airport do direct flights go
to the largest number of other airports?
(e) From which airport do direct flights go
to the smallest number of others airports?

3

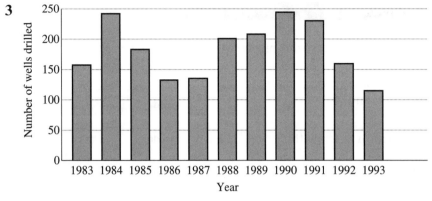

The bar chart shows the number of wells drilled between 1983 and 1993.
(a) In which year were the most wells drilled.
(b) How many wells were drilled in 1988?
(c) How many wells were drilled in 1991?   [E]

4 A survey was done of the times of arrival of the pupils at a primary school. No pupils arrived before 0820 or after 0920 on the day of the survey. The times of the last 20 pupils to arrive are shown below.

0900 0900 0901 0902 0904 0905 0905 0905 0906 0907
0908 0909 0909 0911 0911 0914 0914 0914 0915 0919

The tally chart is filled in except for the last 20 pupils.
(a) Copy and complete the tally and fill in the frequency column.

Time of arrival	Tally	Frequency
At 0820 and before 0825	ЖH	5
At 0825 and before 0830	ЖH III	8
At 0830 and before 0835	ЖH ЖH	10
At 0835 and before 0840	ЖH ЖH	10
At 0840 and before 0845	ЖH ЖH ЖH ЖH ЖH II	27
At 0845 and before 0850	ЖH ЖH ЖH ЖH ЖH ЖH II	34
At 0850 and before 0855	ЖH ЖH ЖH ЖH ЖH ЖH ЖH ЖH II	42
At 0855 and before 0900	ЖH ЖH ЖH ЖH ЖH ЖH I	31
At 0900 and before 0905		
At 0905 and before 0910		
At 0910 and before 0915		
At 0915 and before 0920		

(b) Draw a frequency diagram for those who arrived at 0820 or later.

Altogether, there are 215 pupils at the school.

(c) How many pupils were absent on the day of the survey?

(d) By what time had at least half the 215 pupils arrived?

(e) What time do you think the school starts? Justify your answer.

[E]

5 Here are the weights, in kg, of 30 students.

45, 52, 56, 65, 34, 45, 67, 65, 34, 45, 65, 87, 45, 34, 56,
54, 45, 67, 84, 45, 67, 45, 56, 76, 57, 84, 35, 64, 58, 60

(a) Copy and complete the frequency table below using a class interval of 10 starting at 30.

Weight range (w)	Tally	Frequency
$30 \leqslant w < 40$		

(b) Which class interval has the highest frequency?   [E]

6 120 pupils in a school were given the choice of 4 activities for their PE lessons. The table shows the numbers opting for each activity.

Activity	Number of pupils
Outdoor activity	25
Keep fit	30
Basketball	26
Badminton	39
	total 120

The information is to be shown on a pie chart.

(a) Calculate the sector angle for each activity.
Copy and complete the table below.

Activity	Angle
Outdoor activity	75°
Keep fit	
Basketball	
Badminton	

(b) Draw a pie chart to show the information.

(c) From your pie chart, what fraction of the pupils chose keep fit?   [E]

7 In a town 1800 cars were stolen in a year. The table shows information about the times of day when they were stolen.

Time	Number of cars
Midnight to 6 am	700
6 am to midday	80
Midday to 6 pm	280
6 pm to midnight	470
Time unknown	270

This information can be shown in a pie chart.
  (a) Work out the angle of each sector of the pie chart.
  (b) Construct the pie chart.
  (c) What fraction of the number of cars was stolen between midday and 6 pm. Write your fraction in its simplest form.   [E]

8 Sketches of six scatter diagrams A to F are shown.

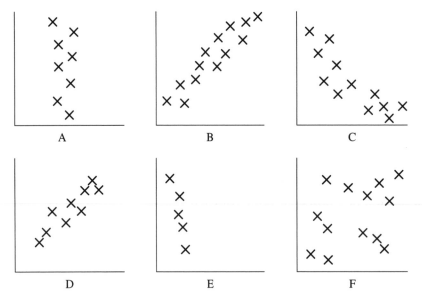

  (a) Which scatter diagrams show
      (i) direct (positive) correlation   (ii) inverse (negative) correlation
      (iii) no correlation?

The table gives information on underground railway (tube) systems in 7 cities.
  (b) Plot a scatter diagram to show this information.

Los Angeles hopes to open an underground railway. There will be 28 km of route.
  (c) Draw a line of best fit on your scatter diagram.
  (d) Use your line of best fit on your scatter diagram to estimate the number of passenger journeys per year? Explain your answer.   [E]

City	Kilometres of route (x)	Passenger journeys per year (millions) (y)
London	395	780
New York	390	1060
Paris	200	1190
Tokyo	155	1930
San Francisco	115	70
Washington DC	125	140
Kyoto	10	45

9 The table shows the number of hours of sunshine and the maximum temperature in ten British towns, on one particular day.

Max. temp (°C)	13	21	20	19	15	16	12	14	14	17
Number of hours of sunshine	11.7	16.7	15.2	15.4	13.2	11.8	9.8	10.2	12.4	13.7

  (a) On a grid plot this information on a scatter graph.
  (b) What does your diagram tell you about the change in the maximum temperature as the number of hours of sunshine increases?   [E]

10 Information about oil was recorded each year for 12 years. The table shows the amount of oil produced (in billions of barrels) and the average price of oil (in £ per barrel).

Amount of oil produced (billions of barrels)	7.0	11.4	10.8	11.3	9.6	8.2	7.7	10.9	8.0	9.9	9.2	9.4
Average price of oil (£ per barrel)	34	13	19	12	23	33	30	12.5	28.5	13.5	26.5	15.5

  (a) Draw a scatter graph to show the information in the table. Use the horizontal axis for amount of oil produced and the vertical axis for average price of oil.
  (b) Describe the correlation between the average price of oil and the amount of oil produced.
  (c) Draw a line of best fit on your scatter diagram.

Test yourself   What to review

If your answer is incorrect, review Foundation book:

1 The examination marks for 40 pupils are shown below.

Mark	0–9	10–19	20–29	30–39	40–49	50–59
Frequency	2	4	12	15	5	2

  (a) Draw a histogram for this data.

  (b) Draw a frequency polygon on your histogram.

  (c) Draw a pie chart for this data.

Unit 10, Section 10.7
Unit 10, Section 10.8
Unit 10, Section 10.8
Unit 10, Section 10.9
Unit 16, Section 16.2
Unit 16, Section 16.2

Test yourself

If your answer is incorrect, review Foundation book:

2 The height and weight of ten pupils are shown in the table.

Weight (kg)	54	59	60	60	63	66	70	71	69	74
Height (cm)	155	160	162	166	169	172	177	180	181	183

(a) Draw a scatter diagram for this data.

Unit 25, pages 325–326
Unit 25, pages 385–388

(b) Describe the correlation between the weight and the height.

Unit 25, pages 326–327
Unit 25, pages 385–388

(c) Draw a line of best fit on your scatter diagram.

Unit 25, Example 1
Unit 25, Example 1

Test yourself answers

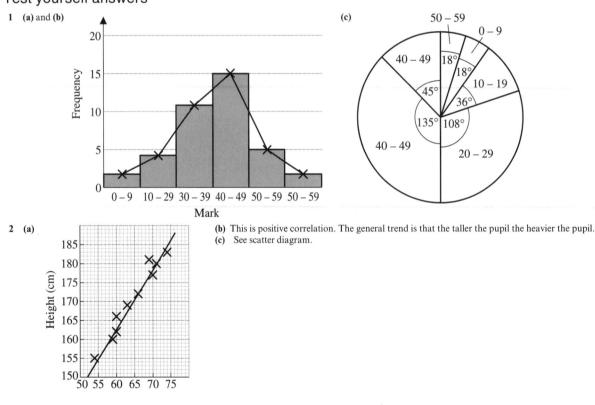

1 **(a)** and **(b)**

(c)

2 **(a)**

(b) This is positive correlation. The general trend is that the taller the pupil the heavier the pupil.
(c) See scatter diagram.

24 Averages

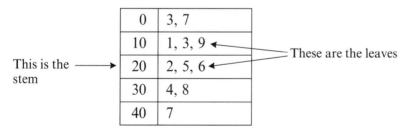
Example

Find the median and mode of:

3, 6, 8, 1, 4, 3, 7, 2, 6, 5, 3

Answer

First arrange in order of size:

1, 2, 3, 3, 3, 4, 5, 6, 6, 7, 8

Using **2**, median is middle value
11 items, so 6th item is middle value
median $= 4$
Using **1**, value occurring most often mode $= 3$

for n items middle item
$= \frac{n+1}{2}$th position

Worked examination question 1 [E]

The list gives the ages, in years, of the Mathematics teachers in a school.

$\qquad$ 34, 25, 37, 33, 26

(a) Work out
    (i) the mean age
    (ii) the range.

In the same school, there are six English teachers. The range of their ages is 20 years.

(b) What do the ranges tell you about the ages of the Mathematics teachers and the English teachers?

Answer

(a) (i) Using **3**, mean $= \dfrac{\text{sum of values}}{\text{number of values}}$

$\qquad\qquad\qquad = \dfrac{34 + 25 + 37 = 33 + 26}{5}$

$\qquad\qquad\qquad = 31$

  (ii) Using **4**, range $=$ highest value $-$ lowest value

$\qquad\qquad\qquad = 37 - 25$

$\qquad\qquad\qquad = 12$

(b) The English teachers have a bigger range than the Mathematics teachers showing a wider spread of age.

Worked examination question 2 [E]

Number of tickets	Number of teachers
0	2
1	7
2	5
3	2
4	0
5	3
6	1

Some teachers were asked how many National Lottery tickets they bought last week.
The results are shown in the table.
(a) Which number of tickets is the mode?
(b) Work out the mean number of tickets.
(c) Find the median number of tickets.

Answer

(a) Using **1** and **6**
the mode $= 1$ as this is the class with the greatest frequency.

(b) Using **5**, $\bar{x} = \dfrac{\Sigma fx}{\Sigma f}$

Add 3rd column fx to table.

Number of tickets (x)	Number of teachers (f)	fx
0	2	$0 \times 2 = 0$
1	7	$1 \times 7 = 7$
2	5	$2 \times 5 = 10$
3	2	$3 \times 2 = 6$
4	0	$4 \times 0 = 0$
5	3	$5 \times 3 = 15$
6	1	$6 \times 1 = 6$
Totals	$\Sigma f = 20$	$\Sigma fx = 44$

$$\text{Mean} = \frac{\Sigma fx}{\Sigma f} = \frac{44}{20}$$
$$= 2.2$$

(c) Using **2**

For 20 items position of middle item $= \dfrac{20 + 1}{2} = 10\frac{1}{2}$

Therefore the median is the average of the 10th and 11th item
These both occur in the 2 ticket class.
Therefore median $= 2$

Revision exercise 24

1 Here are the numbers of people living in the different houses in a short road.

4, 2, 3, 4, 5, 1, 3, 2

(a) Work out the mean number of people per house.
(b) Work out the range of the number of people living in a house. [E]

2 Here are the number of goals scored by a school football team in their matches this term.

3, 2, 0, 1, 2, 0, 3, 4, 3, 2

(a) Work out the mean number of goals.
(b) Work out the range of the number of goals scored. [E]

3 These are the number of goals let in by a goalkeeper, Murray, in the first 10 matches of the season.

    0 3 1 2 4 0 1 1 6 4

(a) Calculate the mean number of goals per match.

(b) What was the range for the number of goals?

Murray was injured for the next four matches and the reserve goalkeeper, Kent, played.
The number of goals let in by Kent had a mean of 3 with a range of 2.

(c) How many goals did Kent let in altogether in these four matches?

Both Murray and Kent are fit for the 15th match.

(d) Write down two statements which might help the manager decide which goalkeeper to choose.   [E]

4 The number of pets in 40 households are given in the table.

No. of pets	Frequency
0	7
1	12
2	8
3	5
4	4
5	3
6	1

(a) What is the mode?   (b) Work out the mean.

(c) Find the median.   [E]

5 The temperature at 11 pm in Clifton was recorded for December 1996 as shown in the table.

Temp °C	Number of days
0	3
1	6
2	4
3	4
4	2
5	8
6	3
7	1

(a) What is the mode?   (b) Work out the range.

(c) Calculate the mean.   (d) Find the median.

6 Ten teams took part in a quiz.
Their scores are shown below.

35, 13, 27, 21, 14, 45, 26, 35, 26, 8.

(a) Work out the mean score.
(b) Draw a stem and leaf diagram for this data.   [E]

Test yourself

What to review

If your answer is incorrect,
review Foundation book:

1 0, 0, 1, 1, 2, 2, 2, 2, 4, 6
For the numbers above calculate:
(a) the mean

Unit 20, Examples 6 and 7
Unit 20, Examples 6 and 7

(b) the median

Unit 20, Example 4
Unit 20, Example 4

(c) the mode

Unit 20, Example 1
Unit 20, Example 1

(d) the range.

Unit 20, Section 20.4
Unit 20, Section 20.4

2 Calculate:
(a) the mean

Unit 20, Section 20.6
Unit 20, Section 20.6

(b) the median
from the following table.

Unit 20, Section 20.6
Unit 20, Section 20.6

No. of bedrooms	Frequency
0	3
1	4
2	6
3	7
4	3
5	1

Test yourself answers

1 **(a)** 2 **(b)** 2 **(c)** 2 **(d)** 6   **2** **(a)** 2.25 **(b)** 2

Non-calculator

If your answer is incorrect review:

1 Write down two different pairs of whose numbers that
multiply together to make 40.   (2 marks)

Unit 2, Key point **2** *and Example 1*

2 Zoe counts the numbers of medals won by 6 countries in a
competition. The results are shown in the table.

Country	Australia	China	Germany	France	U.K.	U.S.A.
Medals	11	14	17	8	12	24

Draw a bar chart to show this information.   (3 marks)

Unit 23, Key point **2**

3 Write down the letters of each of the designs which have line
symmetry.

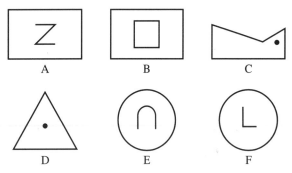

A   B   C

D   E   F   (2 marks)

Unit 19, Key point **1**

4 Owen thought of a number.
He multiplied it by 5.
His answer was 40.
What number did Owen think of?   (2 marks)

Unit 9, Key point **1**

5 Work out the missing numbers in each of these sequences.

(a) 3, 7, 11, ..., 19, 23   (1 mark)
(b) 1, 2, 4, 8, ..., ...   (2 marks)
(c) $\frac{1}{2}, \frac{1}{4}, \frac{1}{8}$ ..., ...   (2 marks)

Unit 10, Key point **5**
Unit 10, Key point **4**
Unit 10, Key point **5**

6 Find the area and perimeter of this shape.

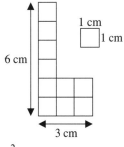

1 cm
1 cm
6 cm
3 cm

Area = ... cm^2 Perimeter = ... cm   (4 marks)

Unit 18, Key points **1** *and* **3**

If your answer is incorrect review:

7 Here are five shapes.

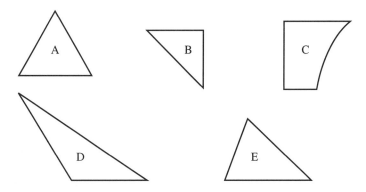

(a) Write down the letters of the shapes which have a right angle. (2 marks)

Unit 16, Key point **2**

(b) Write down two ways in which shape C is different from the other four shapes. (2 marks)

Unit 15, Key points **1** *and* **2**

8 The pictogram below shows the number of pupils absent from Lucea High School one week.

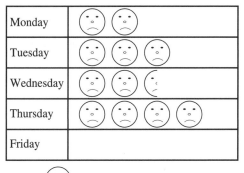

Represents 10 pupils

(a) How many pupils were absent on Tuesday? (1 mark)

(b) How many pupils were absent on Wednesday? (1 mark)

On Friday 15 pupils were absent.

(c) Copy and complete the pictogram to show this. (1 mark)

(d) On which day were there the most pupils absent? (1 mark)

Unit 23, Key point **3**

9 Mrs Mohammed did some shopping.
She bought 5 small items.
The costs of these items were

82p, 95p, 17p, 54p, 52p.

(a) Work out the mean cost of the items. (2 marks)

Unit 24, Key point **3**

(b) Write down the range of the cost of these items. (2 marks)

Unit 24, Key point **4**

(c) Work out the median cost of the items. (2 marks)

Unit 24, Key point **2**

If your answer is incorrect review:

10 A bag contains 8 equal sized coloured balls. 4 of the balls are red, 3 of the balls are blue and 1 of the balls is green.
A ball is taken from the bag at random.
   (a) Which colour is this ball most likely to be?   (1 mark)

Unit 21, Key point **4**

   (b) What is the probability that the ball taken will be
        (i) green
        (ii) blue   (2 marks)   *Unit 21, Key point* **4**

11 Work out:
   (a) $\frac{1}{2} + \frac{3}{4}$ (2 marks)   *Unit 4, Key point* **6**
   (b) $\frac{3}{5} \times \frac{5}{9}$ (2 marks)   *Unit 4, Key point* **9**

12

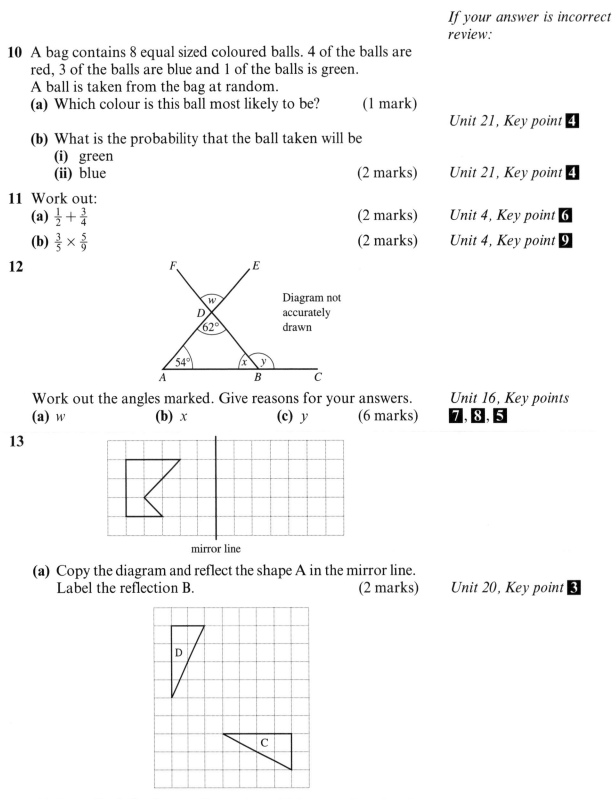

Diagram not accurately drawn

Work out the angles marked. Give reasons for your answers.   *Unit 16, Key points* **7**, **8**, **5**
   (a) w **(b)** x **(c)** y (6 marks)

13

   (a) Copy the diagram and reflect the shape A in the mirror line.
        Label the reflection B.   (2 marks)   *Unit 20, Key point* **3**

   (b) Describe fully the transformation which maps the triangle
        C on to the triangle D.   (2 marks)   *Unit 20, Key point* **2**

If your answer is incorrect review:

14 You must **not** use a calculator.
You must show **all** your working.

   (a) Work out 483×26 (3 marks)   *Unit 1, Example 2*
   (b) Work out $768 \div 24$ (3 marks)   *Unit 1, Example 2*

15 Sandra wins £1500 in a lottery.
She decides to split the money into Saving and Spending.
She does so in the ratio

        Save : Spend $= 3 : 2$

Work out how much of the money she wins, she will save.
                                  (3 marks)   *Unit 7, Key point* **2**

16 There are 720 pupils at Lucea High School.
Dee does a survey to see where they went for the summer holiday.
The results of the survey are shown below, but one result is missing.

Country	No. of pupils
UK	260
Spain	60
France	180
Italy	100
Others	48
Nowhere	...

   (a) Complete the table to show how many pupils went
       'Nowhere' for the summer holiday.   (2 marks)
   (b) Represent the whole of these results on a pie chart.
                                    (4 marks)   *Unit 23, Key point* **4**

17 A solid metal block is in the shape of a cuboid.

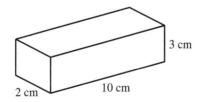

The cuboid measures 2 cm by 3 cm by 10 cm.

(a) Calculate the volume of the metal block.   (2 marks)   *Unit 18, Key point* **8**

The metal block is melted down to make a cuboid with a square base of side x cm and a height of 1 cm.

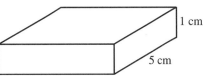

1 cm

5 cm

x cm

(b) Find the value of x.
Give your answer, in cm, correct to one decimal place.
    (3 marks)

Unit 2, Key point **6**

18 The probability of an old car starting on a cold morning is 0.72.
Work out the probability of that old car not starting on a cold morning.   (2 marks)   *Unit 21, Key point* **5**

19 Lucy goes to an aerobics club.
She has to pay the club a joining fee of £70 and then £3 for every session she goes to.
(a) Work out how much it will cost Lucy to join the club and go to 40 sessions.   (2 marks)   *Unit 9, Key point* **3**
(b) Explain how Lucy could work out the cost of joining the club and going to any number of sessions.   (3 marks)   *Unit 9, Key point* **1**

Lucy joins the club and goes to x sessions.
(c) Write down an expression for the total cost of Lucy joining the club and going to x sessions.   (3 marks)   *Unit 9, Key point* **2**

20 $y = 6 - 4x$

(a) Complete the table of values below

x	-3	-2	-1	0	1	2	3
y			10			-2	

    (2 marks)   *Unit 12, Key point* **5**

(b) Draw the graph of

$$y = 6 - 4x$$

for values of x from -3 to 3.   (2 marks)   *Unit 12, Key point* **5**

(c) Use your graph to find
(i) the value of y when $x = 2.25$
(ii) the value of x when $y = 15$ (2 marks)   *Unit 12, Key point* **6**

If your answer is incorrect review:

21 The table lists the value of ten cars and the mileage done by each car.

Value (£)	4000	6500	8000	2000	9000	3500	5500	1000	3000	1500
Mileage (1000 miles)	48	32	15	67	20	64	47	92	75	72

(a) Draw a scatter diagram to show the information in the table.   (3 marks)   *Unit 23, Key point* **8**

(b) Describe the correlation between the value of a car and its mileage.   (1 mark)   *Unit 23, Key point* **9**

(c) Draw the line of best fit.   (2 marks)   *Unit 23, Key point* **10**

(d) Use your line of best fit to estimate the value of a car that has done 55 000 miles.   (2 marks)   *Unit 23, Key point* **10**

22 Solve each of these equations.

Unit 11,

(a) $3x + 1 = 18$ (3 marks)   *Key point* **2**,

(b) $4y - 3 = 2y + 7$ (2 marks)   *Key point* **3**,

(c) $5(z + 8) = 20$ (3 marks)   *Key point* **4**

Calculator

If your answer is incorrect review:

1 (a) Write down the number 3405 in words.   (1 mark)   *Unit 1, Key point* **2**, *Example 1*

(b) Write down 3405 to the nearest ten.   (1 mark)   *Unit 1, Key point* **6**

(c) Write down the value of 4 in 3405.   (1 mark)   *Unit 1, Key point* **1**

2 Here are some patterns of dots:

Unit 10, Key point **1**, *Example 1*

Pattern 1   Pattern 2   Pattern 3

(a) Draw pattern 4.   (1 mark)

(b) Complete the table:

Pattern	1	2	3	4	5
Number of dots	5	9	11		

(2 marks)   *Unit 10, Key point* **5**, *Example 1*

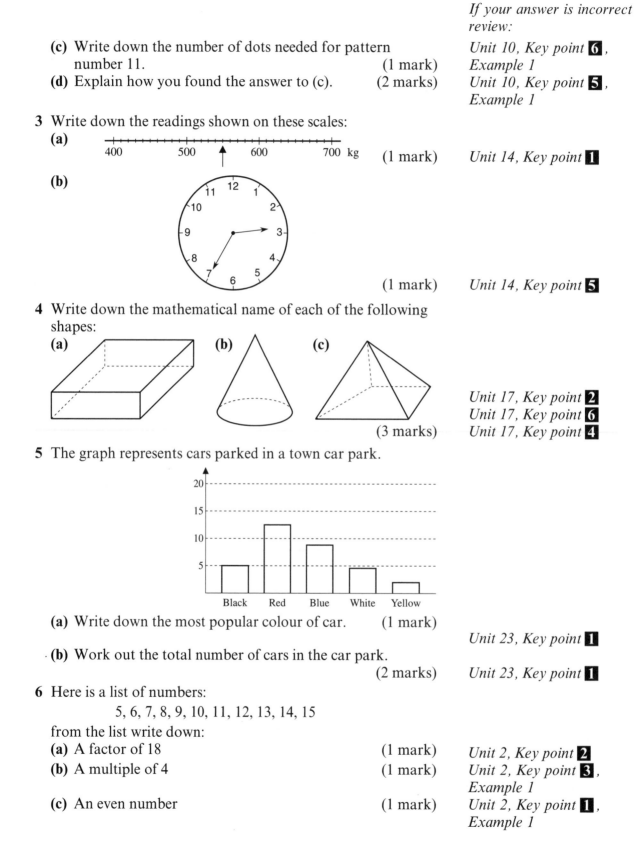

If your answer is incorrect review:

(c) Write down the number of dots needed for pattern number 11. (1 mark)

Unit 10, Key point **6** , *Example 1*

(d) Explain how you found the answer to (c). (2 marks)

Unit 10, Key point **5** , *Example 1*

3 Write down the readings shown on these scales:

(a)

```
400        500        600        700  kg
```

(1 mark)

Unit 14, Key point **1**

(b)

(1 mark)

Unit 14, Key point **5**

4 Write down the mathematical name of each of the following shapes:

(a)   **(b)**   **(c)**

(3 marks)

Unit 17, Key point **2**
Unit 17, Key point **6**
Unit 17, Key point **4**

5 The graph represents cars parked in a town car park.

(a) Write down the most popular colour of car. (1 mark)

Unit 23, Key point **1**

(b) Work out the total number of cars in the car park.

(2 marks)

Unit 23, Key point **1**

6 Here is a list of numbers:

5, 6, 7, 8, 9, 10, 11, 12, 13, 14, 15

from the list write down:

(a) A factor of 18 (1 mark)

Unit 2, Key point **2**

(b) A multiple of 4 (1 mark)

Unit 2, Key point **3** , *Example 1*

(c) An even number (1 mark)

Unit 2, Key point **1** , *Example 1*

If your answer is incorrect review:

(d) A square number   (1 mark)   *Unit 2, Key point* **4**

(e) A prime number   (1 mark)   *Unit 2, Key point* **1**,
Example 1

7

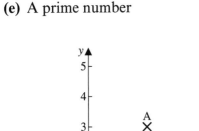

(a) Write down the co-ordinates of the points:

    (i) A   (1 mark)   *Unit 12, Key point* **1**

    (ii) B   (1 mark)   *Unit 12, Key point* **1**

(b) Write down the mid-point of the points AB.   (2 marks)   *Unit 12, Key point* **2**

8 (a) Work out 40% of £65.   (2 marks)   *Unit 6, Key point* **4**

  (b) Work out $\frac{1}{3}$ of £270.   (2 marks)   *Unit 4, Key point* **9**

9 The temperature in Manchester at 4 pm was 8°C. At 2 am it had gone down by −10°C.

  (a) What was the temperature at 2 am?   (1 mark)   *Unit 3, Key point* **5**

By 4 am it had gone down a further 4°C.

  (b) What was the temperature at 4 am?   (1 mark)   *Unit 3, Key point* **5**

At 10 am it had gone up by 5°C.

  (c) What was the temperature at 10 am?   (1 mark)   *Unit 3, Key point* **5**

10 Simplify:

  (a) $x + x + x + x$ (1 mark)   *Unit 8, Key point 3*

  (b) $2y + 5y$ (1 mark)   *Unit 8, Key point 3*

  (c) $2x + 5y + 3y - x$ (1 mark)   *Unit 8, Key point 3*

  (d) $4(3x + 2)$ (1 mark)   *Unit 8, Key point 3*

11 Here is the sketch of a solid:

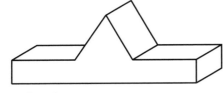

Sketch **(a)** the plan   (1 mark)   *Unit 17, Key point* **10**

       (b) the side elevation   (1 mark)   *Unit 17, Key point* **12**

       (c) the front elevation   (1 mark)   *Unit 17, Key point* **11**

If your answer is incorrect review:

12 Here is a rugby league table:

	Played	Won	Drew	Lost	For	Against
Hull	16	14	0	2	403	96
St Helens	15	12	0	3	327	143
Castleford	16	11	1	4	341	152
Bradford	17	10	3	4	389	239

(a) How many matches have St Helens lost? (1 mark)   *Unit 22, Exercise 22*
(b) Which team has drawn 3 matches? (1 mark)
(c) Which team has scored the least points? (1 mark)
A team receives: 2 points for each match won,
                1 point for each match drawn,
                0 points for each match lost.
(d) Work out the number of points Castleford have.

(1 mark)

(e) A team's difference is found using the rule
difference = for − against
Work out the difference for:
(i) St Helens
(ii) Castleford (2 marks)

13 Work out the size of the angle marked with a letter. Give a reason for your answer.

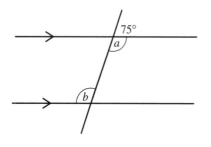

75°
a
b

(4 marks)   *Unit 16, Key points* **5**, **13**

14 (a) Write $\frac{5}{8}$
    (i) as a percentage (1 mark)   *Unit 6, Key point* **5**
    (ii) as a decimal (1 mark)   *Unit 6, Key point* **3**
(b) Write 2.45
    (i) as a mixed fraction (1 mark)   *Unit 4, Key point* **3**
    (ii) as an improper fraction (1 mark)   *Unit 4, Key point* **3**
    (iii) Write 30%, $\frac{1}{4}$, 0.4, $\frac{1}{3}$ in ascending order (2 marks)   *Unit 6, Worked examination question 1*
(c) Work out the value of
    (i) $\sqrt{12.96}$ (1 mark)   *Unit 1, Example 2*

If your answer is incorrect review:

(ii) $\dfrac{26.4 - 18.43}{0.012}$ (1 mark)   *Unit 1, Example 2*

(iii) $(2.3)^3 - 3(\sqrt{5.2 - 2.4})$ (3 marks)   *Unit 1, Example 2*

15 In a survey, the number of bedrooms of 180 houses was recorded.

Bedrooms	Frequency
1	3
2	51
3	87
4	24
5	15

Complete a pie chart to show this information. (4 marks)   *Unit 23, Key point* *, Worked exam question 2*

16 George needs to calculate the answer to 21.32×49.69
   (a) Write down two numbers he could use as approximations to help him estimate this answer. (2 marks)   *Unit 1, Key point* **8**
   (b) Work out the estimate, using these two approximations. (1 mark)   *Unit 1, Key point* **8**
   (c) Work out, correct to the nearest whole number, the difference between the estimate and the exact answer given by a calculator. (2 marks)   *Unit 1, Example 3*

17 In athletics, the discus is thrown from a circle of radius 1.25 metres.
   For the circle calculate
   (a) its perimeter, in metres
   (b) its area, in square metres.
   Give your answers correct to one decimal place. (5 marks)   *Unit 18, Key point* **2** *, Key point* **7**
   Unit 5, Key point **3**

18

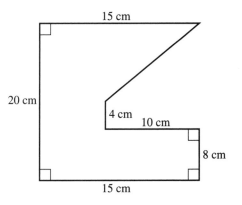

The diagram shows a flat shape.
Work out the area of the shape. (5 marks)   *Unit 18, Key points* **4** *,* **5**

19 Mary goes on holiday to France.
The exchange rate is £1 = €1.64.
She changes £350 into euros.
(a) How many euros does she get? (2 marks) *Unit 12, Key point* **7**
When she gets back home she has €126 left.
The exchange rate is now £1 = €1.59.
(b) How much money in pounds does she get? (3 marks) *Worked exam question 3*

20 Jessica uses the formula
$$p = rh + b \text{ to work out her pay.}$$
Work out her pay when
$$r = 35, h = £4.50 \text{ and } b = £17.75 \qquad \text{(3 marks)} \qquad Unit\ 9,\ Key\ point\ \mathbf{3}$$

21 Enlarge this shape by scale factor 2 from centre $(0, 3)$.

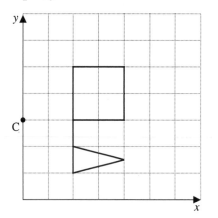

Unit 20, Key point **5**
(3 marks) *Worked exam question 2*

22 Mrs Lucy asked the pupils in her class how long in minutes the journey to college took. The times were:

38, 9, 15, 17, 34, 26, 22, 13, 38, 7, 33, 8, 20
10, 28, 37, 14, 6, 24, 19, 17, 15, 23, 33, 4

(a) Draw a stem and leaf diagram to represent the
information. (3 marks) *Unit 24, Key point* **7**
(b) What was the median time? (1 mark) *Unit 24, Key point* **2**
(c) Calculate the mean time correct to 1 significant figure.
(3 marks) *Unit 24, Key point* **5**

23 Solve $2(3x + 1) = 8$. (2 marks) *Unit 11, Key point* **4**

Answers

Revision exercise 1

1 **(a)** 532   **(b)** 235
2 **(a)** 36 km
   (b) any two distances totalling 75 km
3 8700
4 3404
5 5
6 7, 23, 36, 39, 46, 49
7 **(a)** 5   **(b)** £787.50
8 **(a)** 900 is greater than 670
   (b) 670 + 230
9 **(a)** 40 × 90   **(b)** 3600   **(c)** 49
10 **(a)** 9472   **(b)** 29.78 (to 2 d.p.)
11 45
12 **(a)** 500 × 90, 45 000   **(b)** 200 ÷ 400, 5

Revision exercise 2

1 Any two from 1 × 32, 2 × 16, 4 × 8 or in reverse order.

2 **(a)**

	24	
21	28	35
	32	

(b) The multiples of 8.

3 **(a)** 3, 4, 9, 12   **(b)** 13
4 **(a)** 15, 5, 3, 1   **(b)** 20, 10, 5, 4, 2, 1
   (c) 5
5 Any three from 1 × 30, 2 × 15, 3 × 10, 5 × 6 in either order.
6 **(a)** **(i)** 9010, 68, 764, 390
          (ii) 9010, 85, 390, 105
          (iii) 9010, 390
   (b) Explanation such as
          (i) last digit even
          (ii) last digit a 0 or 5
          (iii) last digit a 0
7 17, 19

Revision exercise 3

1 **(a)** 0   **(b)** −9
2 −7, −5, −3, −2, 1, 4
3 7°C
4 5°C
5

          ─── −5 °C
          ─── −7 °C
          ─── −10 °C

6 **(a)** −5   **(b)** 6
7 8°C
8 **(a)** −20   **(b)** −7   **(c)** 45   **(d)** 3
9 **(a)** 9°C   **(b)** −2°C
10 **(a)** 5°C   **(b)** −5°C

Revision exercise 4

1 **(a)** $\frac{7}{10}$ **(b)** $5\frac{7}{12}$ **(c)** $\frac{5}{12}$ **(d)** $4\frac{1}{10}$ **(e)** $1\frac{1}{8}$
   (f) $\frac{2}{5}$ **(g)** $5\frac{2}{5}$ **(h)** $4\frac{4}{15}$ **(i)** $\frac{2}{3}$ **(j)** $\frac{5}{56}$
   (k) $6\frac{9}{10}$ **(l)** $1\frac{31}{45}$
2 110

3 $\frac{3}{10}$
4 380
5 £3.60
6 15 miles
7 **(a)** 15 minutes   **(b)** 24 minutes
8 **(a)** $\frac{3}{4}$ **(b)** $\frac{2}{3}$
9 £412.50
10 **(a)** $\frac{5}{8}$ **(b)** $\frac{3}{8}$
11 £276
12 **(a)** £14.75   **(b)** 6   **(c)** £2.80

Revision exercise 5

1 0.6
2 3.404
3 1.68 m or 168 cm
4 £165.78
5 22.36 cm²
6 0.625
7 5.064
8 13.12 km
9 **(a)** £470   **(b)** £14.10
10 $\frac{2}{5}$, 0.402, $\frac{43}{100}$
11 £5653.44

Revision exercise 6

1 £196
2 £5760
3 **(a)** £525   **(b)** £3525
4 35%
5 25%, 0.3, $\frac{3}{8}$, $\frac{1}{2}$, 0.6, 67%
6 £24.64
7 588
8 30%
9 400%
10 34%
11 **(a)**

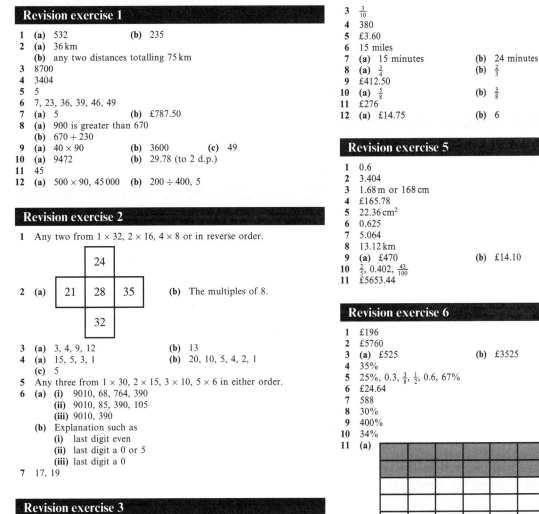

(b) 75%

Revision exercise 7

1 **(a)** 7.5 or $7\frac{1}{2}$ lbs
   (b) 30 ounces flour, 5 ounces cornflour, 15 ounces butter, 20 ounces sugar, 5 eggs.
   (c) 21.3 grams
2 **(a)** £4800   **(b)** £5232   **(c)** £900
3 200 g flour, 25 g sugar
4 1 : 500
5 **(a)** $\frac{4}{7}$ **(b)** 60
6 **(a)** 66 cm   **(b)** 267 km
7 £450
8 **(a)** £76.80   **(b)** £51.20

Revision exercise 8

1 6a cm
2 $m = 4n + 1$
3 **(a)** $4x + 8$ **(b)** $3(2x + 1)$ or $6x + 3$
4 **(a)** $C + P$ **(b)** $2C + P$
5 **(a)** $4a + b$ **(b)** $x + 4y$
6 **(a)** $p + 4q$ **(b)** $2p + 22q$
7 **(a)** £5p **(b)** £np

8 $£\dfrac{N}{5}$ or £0.2N

9 $5(x+1)$ or $5x+5$

10 **(a)** $x+y$ **(b)** $5(x+y)$ or $5x+5y$

11 **(a)** $(x+4)$ cm   **(b)** $P=(4x+8)$ cm

12 **(a)** $3(x+2y)$ **(b)** $a(a+4)$
     (c) $a(5a-1)$ **(d)** $p(7p+1)$

Revision exercise 9

1 **(a)** **(i)** 50   **(ii)** 13   **(iii)** 21.2
    (b) $36=24+3t$

2 **(a)** 26   **(b)** $P=3x+y$

3 **(a)** 3000 kg   **(b)** $L=20P$

4 **(a)** £45   **(b)** $C=25+0.1x$

5 $y=3k-1$

6 **(a)** $P=4x+2$ **(b)** 22 cm

7 $P=20$

8 **(a)** $L=a+2b$ **(b)** 100 cm

9 **(a)** $2<x<5$

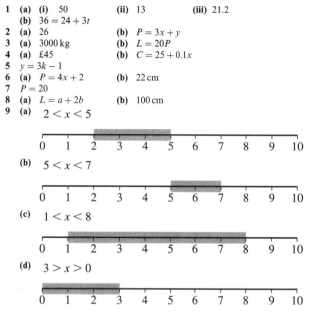

    (b) $5<x<7$

    (c) $1<x<8$

    (d) $3>x>0$

Revision exercise 10

1 **(a)** 65, 59   **(b)** 35

2 **(a)** 24 and 30
    (b) 4th and 5th multiples of 6

3 **(a)** **(i)**

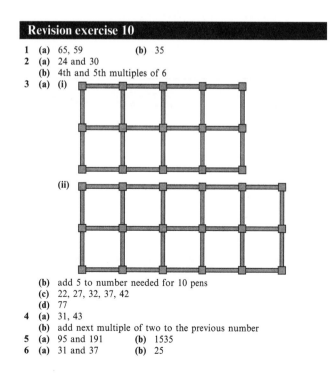

    (ii)

    (b) add 5 to number needed for 10 pens
    (c) 22, 27, 32, 37, 42
    (d) 77

4 **(a)** 31, 43
    (b) add next multiple of two to the previous number

5 **(a)** 95 and 191   **(b)** 1535

6 **(a)** 31 and 37   **(b)** 25

Revision exercise 11

1 **(a)** $x=6\frac{3}{4}$ **(b)** $y=9$ **(c)** $x=6$
    (d) $y=-2$ **(e)** $x=3\frac{4}{5}$ **(f)** $x=10$
    (g) $x=5$ **(h)** $x=11$ **(i)** $x=3\frac{1}{2}$
    (j) $x=7$

2 **(a)** $y=4$ **(b)** $x=-2$ **(c)** $x=-\frac{1}{3}$
    (d) $x=-3\frac{1}{2}$ **(e)** $x=-3$ **(f)** $x=10$
    (g) $x=-\frac{2}{3}$ **(h)** $x=-5$ **(i)** $x=-5\frac{1}{2}$
    (j) $x=2$ **(k)** $x=10$ **(l)** $k=5$
    (m) $p=-3\frac{1}{2}$ **(n)** $x=8$ **(o)** $x=3\frac{1}{2}$

3 **(a)** $y=4$ **(b)** $x=-3$ **(c)** $y=7$

4 **(a)** $x=8$ **(b)** $y=-3$

Revision exercise 12

1 **(a)** **(i)** $(4,6)$ **(ii)** $(9,0)$
    (b)

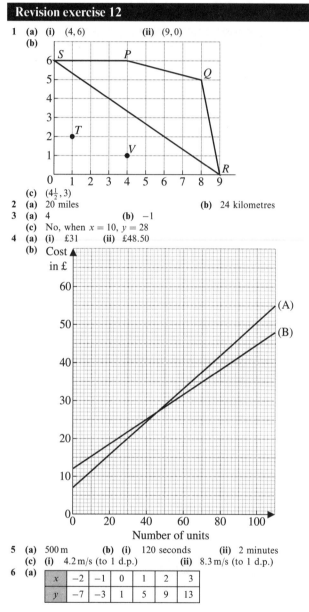

    (c) $(4\frac{1}{2},3)$

2 **(a)** 20 miles   **(b)** 24 kilometres

3 **(a)** 4   **(b)** -1
    (c) No, when $x=10$, $y=28$

4 **(a)** **(i)** £31   **(ii)** £48.50
    (b)

5 **(a)** 500 m   **(b)** **(i)** 120 seconds   **(ii)** 2 minutes
    (c) **(i)** 4.2 m/s (to 1 d.p.)   **(ii)** 8.3 m/s (to 1 d.p.)

6 **(a)**

x	-2	-1	0	1	2	3
y	-7	-3	1	5	9	13

(b) and (c)

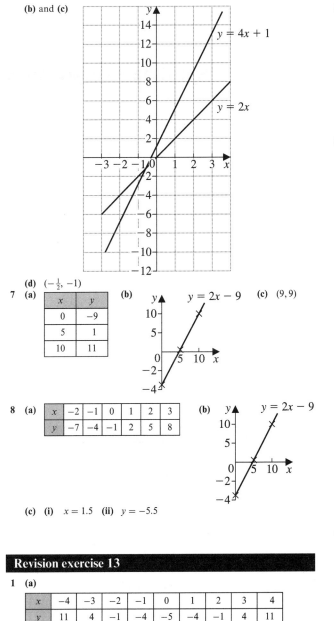

$y = 4x + 1$

$y = 2x$

(d) $(-\frac{1}{2}, -1)$

7 (a)

x	y
0	−9
5	1
10	11

(b)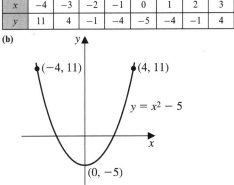

$y = 2x - 9$

(c) $(9, 9)$

8 (a)

x	−2	−1	0	1	2	3
y	−7	−4	−1	2	5	8

(b)

$y = 2x - 9$

(c) (i) $x = 1.5$ (ii) $y = -5.5$

Revision exercise 13

1 (a)

x	−4	−3	−2	−1	0	1	2	3	4
y	11	4	−1	−4	−5	−4	−1	4	11

(b)

$(-4, 11)$ $(4, 11)$

$y = x^2 - 5$

$(0, -5)$

2 (a)

$(-5, 25)$ $(5, 25)$

$y = x^2$

$(0, 0)$

(b)

$(-5, 50)$ $(5, 50)$

$y = 2x^2$

$(0, 0)$

3 (a) and (b)

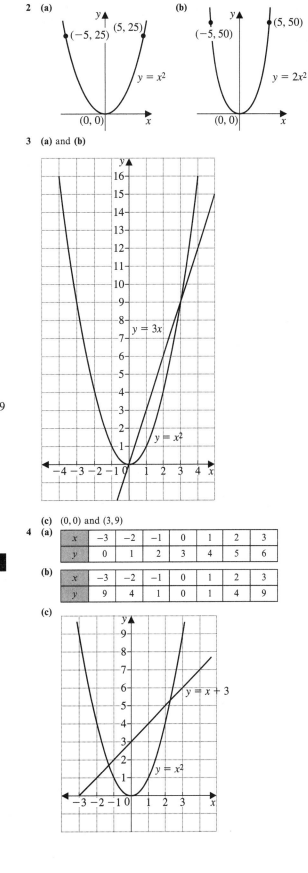

$y = 3x$

$y = x^2$

(c) $(0, 0)$ and $(3, 9)$

4 (a)

x	−3	−2	−1	0	1	2	3
y	0	1	2	3	4	5	6

(b)

x	−3	−2	−1	0	1	2	3
y	9	4	1	0	1	4	9

(c)

$y = x + 3$

$y = x^2$

Revision exercise 14

1 1.87 m
2 1.1 litres
3 (a) 70 mph   (b) −4°C   (c) 1.45 seconds
4 (a) 1.9 kg   (b)

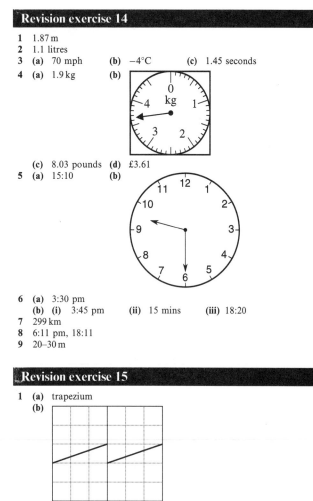

   (c) 8.03 pounds (d) £3.61
5 (a) 15:10   (b)

6 (a) 3:30 pm
   (b) (i) 3:45 pm   (ii) 15 mins   (iii) 18:20
7 299 km
8 6:11 pm, 18:11
9 20–30 m

Revision exercise 15

1 (a) trapezium
   (b)

2 (a)

   (b) rectangle, square   (c) square
3 B and C
4 (a) 36°   (b) 144°
5

6 (a) parallelogram
   (b)

7 (a) 160°
8 It has only 3 sides.
9 (a) (i) yes   (b) (i) yes
       (ii) RHS   (ii) SSS

Revision exercise 16

1 (a) South   (b) East
2 (a) Kendal   (b) Taunton
3 (a) 040°   (b) 135°
4 (a) 135°   (b) angle at D = 55°
5 (a) School   (b) East   (c) North-west
6 (a) 75° Angles on a straight line add up to 180°
   (b) 65° Angles on a straight line add up to 180°
   (c) 100° Angles meeting at a point add up to 360°
   (d) 99° Angles meeting at a point add up to 360°
   (e) f = 55°, e = 125°
        125° and e are vertically opposite; so are f and f. e and f are
        also angles on a straight line, so are f and 125°.
   (f) g = 60°, 2g = 120° Angles meeting at a point add up to 360°.
        6g = 360°.
   (g) 19° Sum of interior angles of a triangle
   (h) 38° Interior angles of a quadrilateral
   (i) 70° Interior angles of a triangle
   (j) 143°, 64° Angles on a straight line
   (k) 40° Vertically opposite angles
   (l) n = 60°, 2n = 120° Interior angles of a quadrilateral
   (m) p = 108°; alternate angles
   (n) q = 114°; corresponding angles
   (o) r = 81°; corresponding angles
        s = 81°; corresponding angles
        t = 81°; alternate angles
   (p) u = 75°; angles on a straight line
        v = 75°; corresponding angles
        w = 75°; vertically opposite angles

Revision exercise 17

1 A, D
2

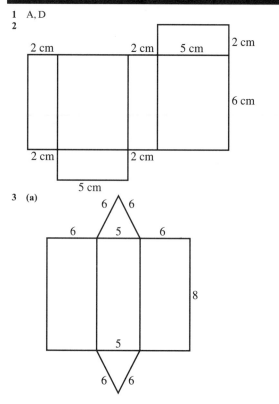

3 (a)

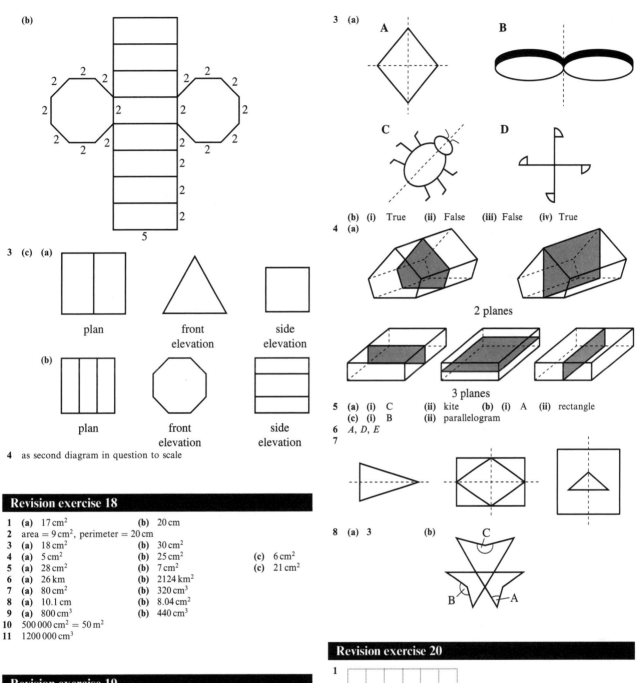

(b)

3 (c) (a)

plan   front   side
              elevation   elevation

(b)

plan   front   side
              elevation   elevation

4 as second diagram in question to scale

Revision exercise 18

1 (a) $17\,\text{cm}^2$ **(b)** $20\,\text{cm}$
2 area $= 9\,\text{cm}^2$, perimeter $= 20\,\text{cm}$
3 (a) $18\,\text{cm}^2$ **(b)** $30\,\text{cm}^2$
4 (a) $5\,\text{cm}^2$ **(b)** $25\,\text{cm}^2$ **(c)** $6\,\text{cm}^2$
5 (a) $28\,\text{cm}^2$ **(b)** $7\,\text{cm}^2$ **(c)** $21\,\text{cm}^2$
6 (a) $26\,\text{km}$ **(b)** $2124\,\text{km}^2$
7 (a) $80\,\text{cm}^2$ **(b)** $320\,\text{cm}^3$
8 (a) $10.1\,\text{cm}$ **(b)** $8.04\,\text{cm}^2$
9 (a) $800\,\text{cm}^3$ **(b)** $440\,\text{cm}^3$
10 $500\,000\,\text{cm}^2 = 50\,\text{m}^2$
11 $1\,200\,000\,\text{cm}^3$

Revision exercise 19

1 (b), (d), (f)
2

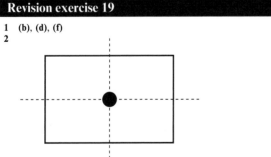

3 (a)

A   **B**

C   **D**

(b) (i) True   **(ii)** False   **(iii)** False   **(iv)** True
4 (a)

2 planes

3 planes

5 (a) (i) C   **(ii)** kite   **(b) (i)** A   **(ii)** rectangle
(c) (i) B   **(ii)** parallelogram
6 *A, D, E*
7

8 (a) 3   **(b)**

Revision exercise 20

1

2 (a)

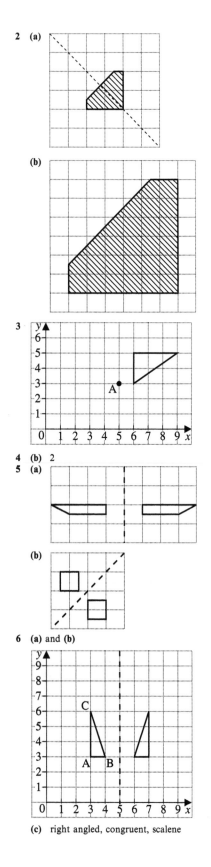

(b)

3

4 (b) 2

5 (a)

(b)

6 (a) and (b)

(c) right angled, congruent, scalene

7 (a)

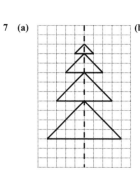

(b) base 10, height 5, area 25
(c) square numbers 1, 4, 9, 16, 25

Revision exercise 21

1 (a) Mint   **(b)** More mints than toffees or pen

(c)

```
    P
 ├────────────┬────────────┤
 0           1/2           1
```

(d)

```
 W
 ├────────────┬────────────┤
 0           1/2           1
```

2 (a) 6 sectors shaded   **(b)** 8 sectors shaded

3 $\frac{11}{12}$

4 (a) 0.7   **(b)** 0.4
  (c) prob > 0.5, therefore more likely to pass than fail

5 $\frac{13999999}{14000000}$

6 (a) $\frac{1}{2}$ **(b)** $\frac{1}{6}$ **(c)** $\frac{1}{49}$

7 (a)

	2	3	4	5
1	1	2	3	4
1	1	2	3	4
2	0	1	2	3
3	1	0	1	2

(b) 1

8 (a) $\frac{1}{6}$ **(b)** $\frac{1}{3}$

(c)

	1	2	3
1	2	3	4
2	3	4	5
3	4	5	6
4	5	6	7
5	6	7	8
6	7	8	9

(d) $\frac{3}{18}$

(e) $P(4) = \frac{3}{24}$, therefore less chance

	1	2	3	4
1	2	3	4	5
2	3	4	5	6
3	4	5	6	7
4	5	6	7	8
5	6	7	8	9
6	7	8	9	10

9 (a) (i) $\frac{8}{13}$ **(ii)** $\frac{5}{13}$ **(b)** YY, YG, GT, GG

Revision exercise 22

1 (a) Morag   **(b)** Samantha   **(c)** Morag
2 (a) 62.8 mpg   **(b)** Rover

3 **(a)** Tonga **(b)** Pins, Arcos Playa
   (c) Siesta, Bougavilla Park
4 Data capture sheet with different vehicles: car, lorry, bus, etc. Tally and frequency.
5 **(a)** A, because it asks the distance travelled to the superstore, and because using 'today' clarifies it.
   (b) It may not be a random sample as not all different types of people shop on Friday evenings.

Revision exercise 23

1 **(a)** 80 **(b)** 50
   (c) Add 1 and $\frac{3}{4}$ golf balls
2 **(a)** Yes, No, Yes **(b)** **(i)** 2 **(ii)** 5
   (c) Bar heights: 1, 5, 5, 2, 2
   (d) Belfast **(e)** Liverpool
3 **(a)** 1990 **(b)** 200 **(c)** 230
4 **(a)** frequencies: 5, 8, 5, 2
   (b) bar chart-height of bars: 5, 8, 10, 10, 27, 34, 42, 31, 5, 8, 5, 2
   (c) 28 **(d)** 0855
   (e) 0900 few arrived after this time
5 **(a)**

Weight range	Frequency
$30 \leqslant w < 40$	4
$40 \leqslant w < 50$	7
$50 \leqslant w < 60$	7
$60 \leqslant w < 70$	8
$70 \leqslant w < 80$	1
$80 \leqslant w < 90$	3

   (b) $60 \leqslant w < 70$
6 **(a)** 75°, 90°, 78°, 117°
   (b)

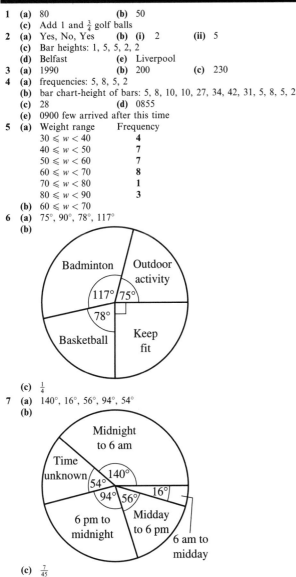

   (c) $\frac{1}{4}$
7 **(a)** 140°, 16°, 56°, 94°, 54°
   (b)

   (c) $\frac{7}{45}$

8 **(a)** **(i)** B, D **(ii)** C, E **(iii)** F
   (b), (c)

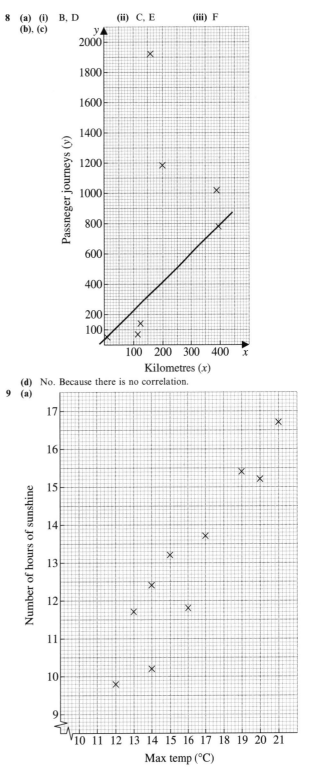

   (d) No. Because there is no correlation.
9 **(a)**

   (b) Maximum temperature increases as number of hours of sunshine increases.

10 (a), (c)

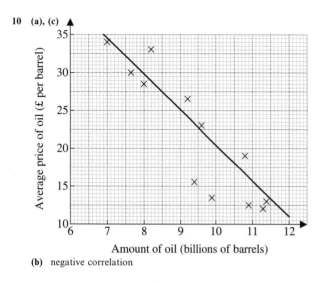

(b) negative correlation

Revision exercise 24

1 (a) 3   (b) 4
2 (a) 2   (b) 4
3 (a) 2.2   (b) 6   (c) 12
    (d) Murray lets in less goals than Kent on average. Kent is more consistent as range is smaller.
4 (a) 1   (b) 2   (c) 2
5 (a) 5   (b) 7   (c) 3.2   (d) 3
6 (a) 25
    (b)

0	8
10	3, 4
20	1, 6, 6, 7
30	5, 5
40	5

Examination practice paper: Non-calculator section

1 Any two from 1×40, 2×20, 4×10, 5×8 (or other way round).
2

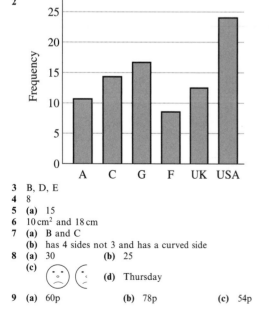

3 B, D, E
4 8
5 (a) 15
6 $10\,cm^2$ and 18 cm
7 (a) B and C
    (b) has 4 sides not 3 and has a curved side
8 (a) 30   (b) 25
    (c) 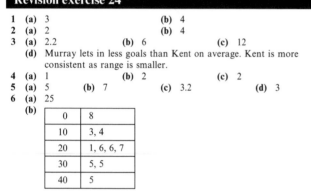   (d) Thursday
9 (a) 60p   (b) 78p   (c) 54p

10 (a) red   (b) (i) $\frac{1}{8}$ (ii) $\frac{3}{8}$
11 (a) $\frac{5}{4} = 1\frac{1}{4}$ (b) $\frac{15}{45} = \frac{3}{9} = \frac{1}{3}$
12 (a) 62° vertically opposite angles
    (b) 64° interior angles of a triangle sum to 180°
    (c) 116° angles on a straight line
13 (a) (d)

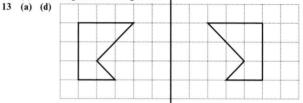

    (b) A rotation, anticlockwise through 90°.
14 (a) 12 558   (b) 32
15 £900
16 (a) 72
    (b)

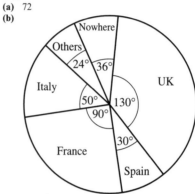

17 (a) $60\,cm^3$ (b) 7.7 cm
18 0.28
19 (a) £190
    (b) No. of sessions ×3, plus 70
    (c) $3x + 70$
20 (a)
21 (a)
22 (a)

x	−3	−2	−1	0	1	2	3
y	18	14	10	6	2	−2	−6

    (b)

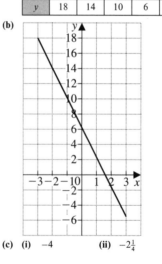

    (c) (i) −4   (ii) $-2\frac{1}{4}$

23 (a), (c)

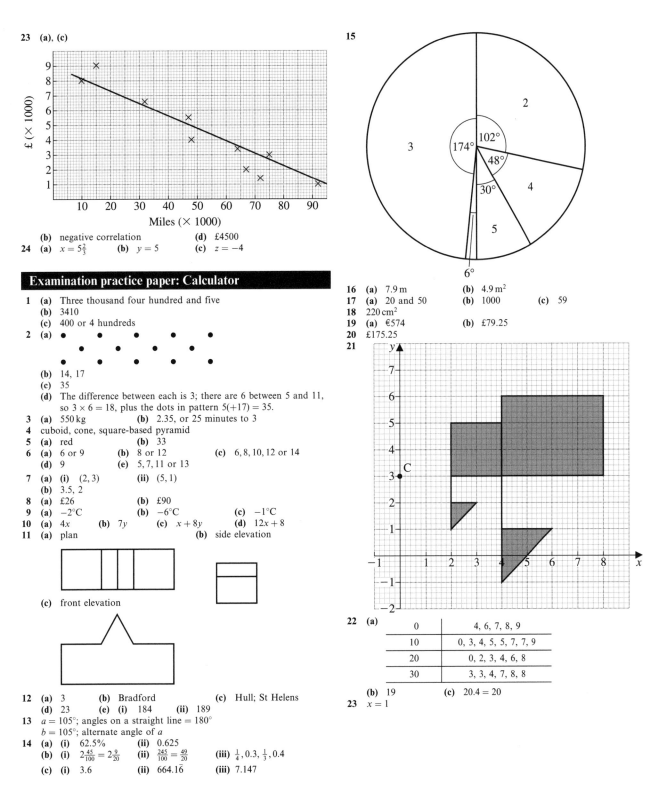

(b) negative correlation   (d) £4500

24 (a) $x = 5\frac{2}{3}$ (b) $y = 5$ (c) $z = -4$

Examination practice paper: Calculator

1 (a) Three thousand four hundred and five
   (b) 3410
   (c) 400 or 4 hundreds
2 (a) [dot pattern]
   (b) 14, 17
   (c) 35
   (d) The difference between each is 3; there are 6 between 5 and 11, so $3 \times 6 = 18$, plus the dots in pattern $5(+17) = 35$.
3 (a) 550 kg   (b) 2.35, or 25 minutes to 3
4 cuboid, cone, square-based pyramid
5 (a) red   (b) 33
6 (a) 6 or 9   (b) 8 or 12   (c) 6, 8, 10, 12 or 14
   (d) 9   (e) 5, 7, 11 or 13
7 (a) (i) (2, 3)   (ii) (5, 1)
   (b) 3.5, 2
8 (a) £26   (b) £90
9 (a) $-2°C$ (b) $-6°C$ (c) $-1°C$
10 (a) $4x$ (b) $7y$ (c) $x + 8y$ (d) $12x + 8$
11 (a) plan   (b) side elevation

[plan view diagram]   [side elevation diagram]

   (c) front elevation

[front elevation diagram]

12 (a) 3   (b) Bradford   (c) Hull; St Helens
   (d) 23   (e) (i) 184   (ii) 189
13 $a = 105°$; angles on a straight line $= 180°$
   $b = 105°$; alternate angle of a
14 (a) (i) 62.5%   (ii) 0.625
   (b) (i) $2\frac{45}{100} = 2\frac{9}{20}$ (ii) $\frac{245}{100} = \frac{49}{20}$ (iii) $\frac{1}{4}, 0.3, \frac{1}{3}, 0.4$
   (c) (i) 3.6   (ii) $664.1\bar{6}$ (iii) 7.147

15

[pie chart with angles: 174°, 102°, 48°, 30°, 6° and sectors labelled 2, 3, 4, 5]

16 (a) 7.9 m   (b) 4.9 m²
17 (a) 20 and 50   (b) 1000   (c) 59
18 220 cm²
19 (a) €574   (b) £79.25
20 £175.25
21

[coordinate grid graph with shaded regions and point C at (0, 3)]

22 (a)

0	4, 6, 7, 8, 9
10	0, 3, 4, 5, 5, 7, 7, 9
20	0, 2, 3, 4, 6, 8
30	3, 3, 4, 7, 8, 8

   (b) 19   (c) 20.4 = 20
23 $x = 1$

Heinemann Educational Publishers
Halley Court, Jordan Hill, Oxford, OX2 8EJ
a division of Reed Educational & Professional Publishing Ltd

Heinemann is a registered trademark of
Reed Educational & Professional Publishing Ltd

OXFORD   MELBOURNE   AUCKLAND
JOHANNESBURG   BLANTYRE   GABARONE
IBADAN   PORTSMOUTH NH (USA)   CHICAGO

© Keith Pledger and David Kent 1997, 2002

First published in 1997

07   06   05   04   03   02
10   9   8   7   6   5   4   3   2   1

ISBN 0 435 53287 1

Copyright notice

Original design by Wendi Watson

Typeset and illustrated by Tech-Set Limited, Gateshead, Tyne & Wear

Printed in Great Britain by The Bath Press, Bath

Acknowledgements

The publisher's and author's thanks are due to Edexcel for permission to reproduce
questions from past examination papers. These are marked with an [E]. The
answers have been provided by the authors and are not the responsibility of
Edexcel.

Every effort has been made to contact copyright holders of material reproduced in
this book. Any omissions will be rectified in subsequent printings if notice is given
to the publishers.